The Gentle Sex

Turbans and headscarves, wicker baskets on their arms, cheerful smiles on their faces . . . and endless patience. These were the obligatory requirements for the dedicated 'queuer' during and after the War. Acting often on no more than a rumour, they would go out and wait in all weathers, clutching ration books and hoping that whatever they queued for would not run out before they reached the front.

I T WAS THE WAR that ruined all our women. At least, that's what the men said. That and all those daft American films they watched sitting in the *Regal* and the *Pavilion*. Or maybe the *Victory* on Upwell Street. With their mouths gaping open at those pampered, over-confident foreign women driving cars and living in their own apartments, using things like refrigerators and phones and acting all independent like.

How the hell do you sustain a proper order of things when the government not only lets 'em see stuff like that, but also actually drafts them into the steelworks to do men's jobs like driving cranes? Or welding and drilling? Or chucking drunks off of the trams? Surely we could have licked Hitler in the old-fashioned way. With men doing the fighting and working hard and women doing . . . well . . . what women are supposed to do. Couldn't we?

Well, I don't know, I was only a kid at the time. I suppose it did give the women a fresh outlook. Did make them look again at what they previously had accepted as their lot in life. They probably blinked in that sudden bright light of equality, looked back at what they had been used to and said, 'Sod that for a tale, there's more to this life than stopping at home hitting the kids, starching collars, making hash and dumplings and fetching the old feller's suit back from the pawnshop every Friday tea-time'.

Veronica Lake didn't do that, or Greer Garson. They had Alan Ladd or Walter Pidgeon to light cigarettes for them, take them to swish restaurants and call them sweet names, like 'honey' or 'darling'. Not much chance of that when you were up to your armpits in soap suds doing the wash in the 'peggy' tub. Listening to Vera Lynn or Anne Shelton on the wireless and wondering if there was any truth in the rumour that the Co-op might have a few cigarettes that week for 'special' customers. It wasn't like that in the films.

I suppose at this point I should stress that there was a different order of things between the sexes forty or more years ago. There was where we lived, anyway. Believe me, the predominant male attitude then was far more inclined towards protecting His Image than the emancipation of the 'old lass', and it never even entered his head that they should attain the level of the film stars previously mentioned. Why should it? 'I married her,' he'd say, 'I keep her . . . what more does she want?'

Perhaps it was the type of work which engendered it. Hot, heavy, and often dangerous. Cursed with unsociable hours. Or was it the code demanded of him in the blatantly chauvinistic beer-swilling confines of the steelworks, pits and the working men's clubs? Whatever, the introduction of women to do men's work was a dangerous and retrograde step. One to threaten and attack the very core of a 'normal' marriage. No wonder so many shirt-laps were getting scorched or stuck fast in the mangle. That's what the men said. And us kids kept quiet about it 'cos they all wore big belts.

Joking aside though, it really didn't make any difference what they said, or thought. The old way couldn't take precedence over a war.

Places needed filling if the effort was to succeed. And Churchill cared more for steel than he did for shirt-laps. A new order of things had begun. From necessity as much as progress. One that would bring with it social changes to both industry and traditional family life. It would brush aside the limits within which our mothers had lived, and set new patterns for the future. 'Fetch yer own suit back lad . . . I'm going to get a Page Boy perm,' they said defiantly. And as the men drank their beer and moaned about such things, I've no doubt that Old Father Time wet himself laughing at them and their injured pride.

It is without doubt one of the greatest social changes which men of my age or more have witnessed. And so it should be. I for one could never support that old bigoted view that a woman should 'know her place'. Even though I grew up in an environment steeped in such an anachronism. Today their 'place', subject to educational status or talent, of course, is where they choose to make it. And again, so it should be. Clearly then I do not bemoan the change we have seen, rather do I applaud it as a sensible justification of what is right. However, being perfectly honest I cannot air these views without once again looking back fondly on two of those women from my childhood. Two who I will always include in my personal Hall of Fame whenever we recall those times. And remember the characters.

And Daisy Barret was certainly one of those.

Daisy, obviously nick-named 'Upsi', lived in Huntsman's Gardens, so could hardly be classed as one of our lot in Salmon Pastures. All the same, we knew her well. Especially the menfolk. Because Upsi, to everyone's astonishment and annoyance, had the distinctly original habit of roaming the darkened streets of Attercliffe (after getting tanked up on vast amounts of Pimms) looking for a man . . . to fight. True. Ridiculous maybe, but true. There she was, well into her forties and hardly five-and-a-half feet high, yet blessed with the frightening ability of being able to put together clusters of accurate punches good enough to make grown males walk the other way. Not all of them, mind you . . . but enough. We were safe enough, being kids. I suppose she considered anyone of our size as being far too puny to provide her with a decent scrap. But a grown man? Ah . . . that was different. He was fair game. An opportunity to rid herself of the pent-up aggression which manifested itself with the powerful drink.

There had to be a reason for it. After all, you don't usually come across middle-aged women deriving a relief of some sort from street fighting do you? I was also aware that women of that age go through a 'funny' phase. A time when their normality is affected. Likewise their behaviour and well-being. But, as any feller down there at that time would confirm, there was nothing either normal or funny about being caught on the ropes by Upsi.

I remember that she was unmarried and that she lived with her widowed father, Cyril. And perhaps it was that, not being married I mean, and possibly feeling denied a full life of her own, which fed this unnatural urge to lay her hands on a man in a far from loving way. Or was it that the potent drink brought to the surface attributes not normally dormant within her sex? I don't know. I do know that after she caught and pasted, poor old F . . . F . . . F . . . Freddie Thorpe one Bank Holiday Monday, you couldn't have found a bloke this side of Templeborough who'd have lit a fag for her, never mind consider sharing a marriage. Poor old stuttering, inoffensive Freddie had left the *Dog and Duck* pub just after ten that night to make the short (and what would have been safe) walk home. Yet it was after eleven-thirty before Ria, his wife, found him propped up, in a sitting position in Curly Bradshaw's shop doorway.

Now Ria, after clattering on the pub doors and dragging Billy Whittaker the landlord with her to witness what she had found, went hysterical. And if you have read my earlier work in which I described her affliction of creating excess saliva and spraying it around wholesale, then you'll see that the incident was far more traumatic for Billy, seeing as how he couldn't avoid the rampant spit, than it was for the luckless Fred.

'Who'd done it?' Sam Duffy had gaped as Billy related all the grisly details the following night to a crowded bar.

'Upsi,' he'd growled, still feeling damp, courtesy of Ria.

'Upsi Daisy?' asked Alf Skinner, surprised. 'How do yer know?'

'Told us, didn't he?' Billy had glared, annoyed that anyone should doubt his word after suffering the tidal wave of her distress. 'She just grabbed him,' he went on, 'as he went past Owen's entry . . . tried to drag him down it . . . just about ripped half his shirt off afore he got away and run back past here . . . sez he tried to bang on our door for me to fetch our dog out . . . but he daren't stop, poor sod, out of his mind wi' fright he were . . . she's hammered him reight enough,' he concluded, red-faced from not drawing a breath.

'She wants locking up,' Sam had snapped, gaining several nods of approval.

'Either that or turning professional,' said Alf, straightfaced, adding, 'What about Ria? What did she say when yer found her?'

'Enough to bring him round,' said the disgusted Billy. 'I know she nearly drowned me . . . don't know why she can't learn sign language,' shooting ferocious looks at anyone rash enough to find anything remotely funny in all of this.

'Didn't anybody hear owt? . . . didn't he shout or summat?' asked Sam, puzzled at all of this.

'How the bleeding hell do yer shout for help when yer stutter as bad as him? Specially when she's bending yer ribs.' Billy had snorted in disgust then defied any more questions on the subject, concluding that anyone else daft enough to fall foul of her was on their own.

'I'll hit her wi' a pick handle if she ever comes for me,' he ended.

It goes without saying that her behaviour ultimately brought her into contact with the law. And if I remember right it happened when she pounced on two youths making their way home along Broughton Lane after they'd been to see Jane (the one in the Daily Mirror) doing her famous nude poses at the *Attercliffe Palace*.

I imagine their senses and imaginations must have been flooded with lust for that unattainable body as they strolled along, re-living every unblinking second that she had been on view.

And I suppose that being in such a euphoric state of bliss they would have been unprepared for the attack which was launched without warning from what they took to be a merry old soul making her way home, too.

There's even the outside chance that they recognised her, and fancied the odds, seeing as there were two of them. Younger, and having a surfeit of adrenalin pumping away from what they had previously seen. Whatever, she duffed the pair of 'em — to such an extent that the bobbies fetched Dr. Hudson to Attercliffe police station after the victims were brought in by their incensed parents.

Anyway, they locked Upsi up, sent a man to fetch Cyril from the Radical Club where he was concert secretary, and wished to Christ that Upsi would develop a craving for Bovril instead of the deadly concoction which brought out the physical side of her nature.

For his part, Cyril recognised that whatever it was that lay deep within her, waiting to be activated, was totally beyond the lecturings and threats that he had made.

And he argued that, this particular failing aside, his daughter possessed many commendable qualities. In fact, without her his life as a widower would be far less comfortable. But as to her unusual outburts . . . well, it baffled him.

So, the authorities stepped in. And arranged for Upsi to attend a special clinic once a week at the City General Hospital on Herries Road.

Daft as it sounds, it was the best thing that could have happened to her. Because it was through those visits that she met a feller called Ernest Roper who worked on the hospital boilers.

And the last I remember hearing of her was that he'd married her and took her to live with him near the *Magnet* pub on Southey Green. Whether it lasted or not I don't know. Or whether the clinic calmed her anti-social tendencies.

If it didn't . . . well, all I can say is that there must have been some rare old bouts between them. What with Upsi's footwork and Ernest's big biceps from shovelling all that coke.

Choose what, we saw no more of her. And going for a drink down our way became much safer.

Now, 'Becky' Noonan was the other one. Direct relation (so she claimed) to an Irish Romany King.

Held in complete awe by every woman for miles around for her gift of reading tea-leaves, and her knowledge of nature's remedies for everything from straightening out bent toes to slowing down over-sexed husbands. If you wanted to know what was coming . . . go to Becky. If you wanted to know what had gone . . . go to Becky. And should you want to know if someone who'd gone had got there alright, again, go to Becky.

For half-a-crown you had the privilege of drinking from her 'special' bone china tea cup. And the absolute benefit of her 'gift' to interpret what the senseless shapes created by the dead leaves in the bottom of it foretold. Children's futures, money, health, unknown rivals or enemies, where you'd find grandma's missing insurance policy, strangers entering your circle, travel, extra-marital prospects etc, were all in there. Along with anything else that made the client believe she was getting her money's worth. That was her gift. Her Romany heritage, if you believed her that is.

Old Dr Hudson played hell if her name was mentioned in his presence. He'd have gleefully had her ritually burned had it been lawful. Mind you, you could well understand his annoyance of her influence upon the women. Because as a qualified practitioner it must have made his old stethoscope rot to be called out at 3 am on a winter's morning only to find that his earlier medicinal recommendations to the patient had been ignored in favour of one of Becky's 'naturals'. I'm sure she had shares in that herbalist stall in the old Rag and Tag Market down Dixon Lane. Because that's where she sent everyone to get those obscure ingredients which she prescribed. Yet surprisingly, they often worked.

Sleeping with a woman's used silk stocking tied around a sore throat would bring a marked degree of ease from it by the morning. Providing, as the joke went, that you made sure the leg wasn't still inside it.

The leaves of a comfrey plant boiled and made into a poultice reduced large swellings and eased sprains as if by magic. And a red hot poker, or piece of coke from the fire, immersed into a cup of ginger ale cured stomach upsets, and so on.

Toothache, spots, insomnia, colic, bedwetting and a hundred other different ailments all had a remedy. And Becky knew of it. Becky knew everything and sometimes nowt. Because her trick of avoiding losing face or credibility when a cure didn't work and old Hudson had to apply more scientific methods was to smile broadly, twist her head knowingly, tap one finger onto the side of her nose and let out a long 'Aaaah'. As if to say that mere mortals like us were not privy to such things. Only Becky . . . related to a Romany King.

Obviously, as with all controversial characters, there were those who didn't like her. Those who ridiculed her remedies and decried her clairvoyant claims. And some of them had good cause to.

Doris Trotter was one.

She crossed Becky's palm with a month's clothing coupons during the war to ask whether she would ever see her husband Dennis again after he'd been reported missing, presumed killed, in the Western Desert.

Becky, after going through the aforesaid ritual of making sense out of the meaningless mess in the special cup, assured her that he was alive, but hurt and being held in a German P.O.W. camp.

Now Doris had greeted all this with mixed feelings. Relieved, obviously, that he was still alive and sorry that he was hurt. Yet a wee bit narked also. This was due in part to her getting rather heavily involved with the owner of the chip shop she worked in at Darnall terminus.

Thoughts of accepting his open offer of marriage (should she ever be free), along with sharing the lucrative business, had long filled her mind. And what with Dennis's long absence in the land of flies and pies, had tended to put a strain on her marriage vows.

But while-ever he was alive and doing his bit for King and Country, well . . . She couldn't, could she?

So she didn't. And the chip shop owner went and married a red-headed bird who was an oxy-acetylene burner at Firth Browns and came in his shop every day.

And *she* wasn't the shrinking violet type either. Within a week, she had off-loaded her new husband's former fancy on the principle that: 'The only three penn'orths he'll be dishing out from now on'll be in a bag'. And poor old Doris was out on her ear.

Then, to cap it all, she got a visit from a bobby to say that Dennis's whereabouts had been established. He'd apparently turned up in Benghazi, and then managed to get himself very dead after being stabbed by an upset Arab bent on revenging his mother who had just been violated by two Scots Guards.

Well, Doris went wild. And you couldn't blame her. She'd believed every word she'd been told. Even gave a chip shop up. All through Becky.

But she wouldn't wear it when Doris confronted her. Or give the coupons back. And she ended the screaming match, which had fetched the whole street out to listen, by whipping out her famous black cat's foot and threatening to make poor old Doris totally bald.

Strange as it seems, failures such as this didn't diminish her standing amongst the majority of women. It's funny, but whatever it was that she had, be it her alleged connections or her tin-pot cures or her questionable prophecies, Becky Noonan enjoyed everything it brought her. I believe she's well into her nineties by now. But then again, I wouldn't put money on it, knowing her track record with herbs and tea leaves.

If she is, dead I mean, then I've no idea where she finished up. We were all sent to many different areas when progress ate its way through the old East End. She could be laid anywhere. Perhaps even back in the misty land of her supposed Romany folk.

But wherever she is, I bet the old bugger's still getting away with it.

Peter Stringfellow's Mojo Club in Pitsmoor attracted hordes of young people who loved it, and danced and cavorted to pop groups (many of which went on to become famous), surrounded by mirrored walls off which the music bounced to the irritation of local residents. Eventually a petition was organised, complaining that the club's attractions included fighting, sexual activity and even drugs, so the police closed it down.

For those who preferred their music more sedate, the Library Theatre held free weekly lunchtime recitals of recorded music.

2 Best of order

IN THE LIGHT of all that has gone, all that has changed, it is a remarkable testimony to the deep allegiance felt by their members that Working Men's Clubs should still survive to this day. Especially when you note the vast differences in alternatives available now, compared to forty or fifty years ago.

Admittedly they've altered somewhat, but then is that not to be expected? Would present generations be willing to accept the often spartan like amenities of those times?

I think not.

Not when pubs and nightclubs are purpose-built so as to lure the discerning customer into a luxurious stupor as they pay ridiculous prices.

Not for them the round wooden tables and hard back-aching stools. Or the bare concert room floors complementing the oft-times dubious attempts at synchronisation going on between a yellow-keyed piano and a set of drums older than the feller playing them. Producing chords and rhythm patterns, never in a thousand years envisaged by the composer as being the melody he'd had in mind when he'd first written it, as they provided our orchestral needs. And at that I am being more than generous in describing their efforts. For what they did to decent music each weekend accompanying those paid to entertain us was a violation upon the listener, and a downright liberty against those relying upon them for musical aid.

Here, I am referring of course to the 'turns'. Those masochists of the boards who, if female, invariably sang songs such as *Velia* or *We'll Gather Lilacs* in a tremulous voice. Bringing a touch of elegance to their act by wearing evening dresses complete with long black gloves and sparkling earrings. They never ceased to smile, not even on the high notes, despite the musical genocide being committed on their behalf, and proved what a two-faced business they were in by paying tribute at the end for the 'excellent accompaniment' they'd had. Despite the fact that the pair of 'em had done their level best to throw her off key fifteen times.

Or they were the male popinjays, making all the women fidget nervously as they wooed them surreptitiously with the latest ballads. Sickening the drably-garbed husbands in the audience with their blatant display of Burton-assisted narcissism and phoney American accents.

'Bloody poof,' the men would growl aloud, or 'I'd like to see that chuff wi' a pick in his hand.' And so forth, all presented with deep scowls and equally deep and rapid jerks of their Adam's apple as they swallowed yet another pint.

Believe me, it wasn't unknown for a particularly obnoxious specimen to get his trouser turn-ups filled in the gents by someone deliberately misdirecting his unwanted excess.

Ruined suede shoes in no time, did that.

Only a comedian, or perhaps a speciality act such as a ventriloquist could then retard the rate of their liquid intake. And he had to be good. Especially the dummy. In fact you could guage their appreciation simply by the frequency of their glasses being lifted. The better the act . . . the less they drank. And anyone good enough to ground the ale for more than three minutes should have been topping the bill at the *Empire*, because he was too good for our place, that's a fact.

Ask any old-time entertainer whose background had taken in clubland. Some of them would rather endure the ordeal of having all their teeth out rather than repeat the experience.

They'd tell you of concert secretaries whose verbosity down a badly-tuned microphone, giving out regular piercing shrieks, was only matched by their total lack of feeling for the on-coming artist's confidence.

One can only imagine what they must have gone through as they waited in the tiny changing-rooms off-stage listening to these abberrations of a compère prepare the audience for them.

'Right then,' they would holler through the unstable amplification, 'Yer allus telling us to get some good turns for yer, well we've got one. I think so anyway, calls hersen Elizabeth Day, she's a

7

singer.'

'I think yer'll like her, yer better had, she's costing us two pound ten, just for toneet! I've teld her, if she's any good we'll have her back at Christmas. So shurrup! Don't serve any more crisps behind that bar for a bit now, Eddie.'

'So c'mon, put yer hands together for Elizabeth, best of order now, *please!*'

Can you imagine trying to recreate a facsimile of that in today's world of entertainment, when participants now fill the stage with a fortune's worth of electronic help?

Grief, they spend more time tuning everything in with endless repetitions of 'one . . . two . . . one . . . two . . .' than the old-timers got in which to perform their entire act.

But then, today's members are too involved in the complexities of marking Bingo tickets to notice what's going on in that area. Or to feel the traditional numbness of the bum from sitting too long on those hard stools.

And do you know why?

It's because shouting 'House!' is the finest pain-killer known to the working class now. It makes Valium look like an aphrodisiac. It does in today's clubland anyway. What a shame, what a crying shame, for working men's clubs were formed to benefit the community, not as a sop to those whose greed overcomes their sense. Those who would deny others the simple pleasure of conversation as they pray to every known god that their numbers will come out before anyone else's.

To be a member was something a father promised his sons, something to look forward to, and not just for the cheaper beer they sold either, but for *all* the benefits which a club could bring.

The companionship of others, the entertainment, the fishing and pigeon and whippet factions. The indoor and outdoor leagues of crib, darts, dominoes and football creating pride in your club's performances. The free and easy dances bringing in affilliated members from all over and turning strangers into friends. Pensioners being cared for,

and best of all for us kids, the annual outing to the coast.

The club trip.

Looking back now, how do you envisage just how much that one solitary chance each year of seeing the sea meant to us? But it did. Believe me, it did. It was one of those special, count the days off treats, just like Christmas is. A day to savour after weeks, nay months of excited anticipation after receiving your treasured ticket. The date of your going would be clearly printed on it, along with your destination and your charra number, burning itself indelibly into your mind.

The tempo would increase as friend after friend announced with delirious whoops that they had got theirs too. Comparing their coach number with yours and everyone elses. Only we didn't call them coaches then, we called them charras, SUT charras. Poor relations of today's supa-dupa, video, toilet, hostess, air-conditioned road cruisers I admit. But to us, magic. Big comfortable magic carpets, ready and waiting to whisk all of us off to the giddy delights of Cleethorpes or Skeggy, occasionally even Bridlington.

Wide-eyed, we would speed through the early morning flat misty Lincolnshire countryside, seeing countless fields with animals in them like cows or sheep, and huge haystacks, standing there like giant ships marooned in a sea of earth. Delicious anticipation in knowing that each of these rustic wonders which we gazed at brought us that bit nearer to the best treat of all, the sea.

Foot banging, chair bouncing, cheers as the first sighting of your allotted destination appeared on the signposts flashing by. Accompanied by loud chants of 'Cleethorpes, Cleethorpes here we come!' Or whatever the Shangri-La of the day might be.

And then we'd be there.

Every one of us pressing expectant faces to the windows, clambering over each other in a desperate bid to be first to see those elusive waves. Inner torment as we slowly made our way through the town towards the coach park, passing shops whose outsides were covered with all the paraphernalia necessary for a proper appreciation of the beach. Buckets, spades, coloured balls, picture postcards, hats, kites, cricket bats, a whole plethora of cheap simple pleasures. But not for us, not on a club trip.

Our day was to be one of speed, an itinerary of haste, designed to see as much as possible before time ran out, and the magic carpet whisked us all back. I remember how the stewards in charge delayed us, unnecessarily we thought, to check that our identifying tickets were firmly attached to our coat lapels before thrusting packets of sandwiches and small bottles of pop into our hands as a make-do lunch. Hands that were more anxious to use the free tickets to Wonderland which they handed out as well. Six free rides on the dodgems, ghost train, Pop-Eye's moonrocket, hoopla or the awesome Shamrock. Supplemented by five bob to splash out on ice cream, rock, toffee apples and still more pop.

Oh, the great whooping, yelling charge, as they finally set us free from their anxious jurisdiction. Screaming out to us not to get hurt or lost or to forget the name of the fish restaurant we all had to congregate at for our tea at four-thirty. Hoping that their instructions would somehow find a way of penetrating young minds completely obsessed with better things.

It would be almost twelve-thirty as we sped the short distance to the sea front, and I guarantee that we'd all be flat broke, ticketless and deflated before it reached two. Only then would we go to see the beach and the grey cold-looking sea properly, to fill in the remaining time before the fish and chip rendezvous. Two-and-a-half empty, skint, pebble-skimming, sea- paddling, sand-kicking hours in which to get fed up, hopefully asking everyone we met from our trip if they should possibly have any unused free tickets left. To no avail. It was the anti-climax of the day, the bursting of the dream, the reality that seaside places were not such a paradise after all, not if you had nowt to spend. They were places where your little bit of money disappeared much more quickly than the clock moved, and

VICTORY!
In May 1945 the residents of Buttermere Road celebrated the end of the war in Europe with flags, bunting and victory signs, and the inevitable street party. Women and children really were dancing on the cobbles, for the men were still away at the war. In those far-off days we burned effigies of Hitler on bonfires and sang the National Anthem with great gusto.

having gone, leaving you feeling vulnerable, even cheated.

Looking back, I suppose those empty frustrating hours we killed waiting for our tea on days like that were an early taste of what life would hold for us later on. A prelude if you like, that real life, not the glossy film or imagined one, was full of letdowns. Full of false delights which excited you and drew you on only to dance away like some fickle maiden just when you needed re-assuring, when you were far from home and skint. The sea would no longer hypnotise you, the sandy beach an irritant that got inside your socks. The sights and sounds of the amusements being used, of others using them in your place, would make you feel left out, denied what should have been a full day's fun.

A lonely, hurt-filled time, to bear until the fish and chips were ready.

No wonder the three-hour journey home was always more subdued than our arrival. Eyes were heavy from the early start, stomachs would complain over the unfair mixture of treats they had been forced to digest, and spirits would be low due to the day lasting longer than the means to finance it. The vibrations of the charra would stimulate those of a puny constitution into the inevitable disgrace of being sick, creating furious rows between the driver about the mess, and the stewards who accused him of failing to make necessary stops despite their demands. Whoever was right was secondary really, what did matter was that the results of these rejections stopped us from running up and down the aisle without risking a broken leg.

The arrival back at the parent club would stir us all into a bout of cheering and verses of, 'She'll be coming round the mountain when she comes' with the more bolder ones substituting the ruder version of that popular song of the time, and earning withering looks from the stewards for our audacity at infringing what they considered to be the sole property of the grown-ups.

Hordes of mums and dads anxiously scanned each arriving charra for their Albert or Herbert or Sarah or Billy, and there was the comfort of knowing that you were back in dear old dirty Sheffield. The day out over, the adventure complete, the overwhelming tiredness that motion, excitement and fresh air always brings, making eyes droop as you forced tired legs to carry you home through those dark streets.

'It were great mam,' you would yawn, feeling her hand clutching yours tightly. 'Great . . . even t'sun came out'.

God bless those old east coast fore-runners of today's charter flights winging us away to sunny Spain, giving us the chance of wallowing for two weeks in duty-free delusions of grandeur.

Costa del Cleethorpes was never like this. You never see a single kid with a club ticket pinned to him, or running about like mad clutching a fistful of free ride tickets in one hand and a toffee apple in the other. Those business-like Spaniards wouldn't accept them on the pedalos anyway. Ah well . . . times change and traditions die, even the good ones. Working men's clubs gave my childhood lasting memories, gave me a brief, once-a-year look at that magical thing called the seaside, and no Mediterranean hotspot has ever evoked within me the sleepless excitement of counting the days as they did. They gave me something which I couldn't afford, not something that I could.

I think of this often whenever I go into a club now, and inwardly fume at the slavish devotion which I see being paid to those numbered balls spewing forth from that moronic bingo machine. A child's game elevated to an obsession by those old enough to know better. And I feel for the streets which once played host to forty or more charras, each one full to the brim with eager kids. Streets that are now lined with private motor cars, their juvenile-minded owners all inside the club anxiously marking their tickets.

'Yer house is on fire Tommy'

'Sod the house! I only want one more number'

Eyes down, look in.

Forget the past. This is for the jackpot.

W HAT BECAME of our ragmen? Those cloth-capped 'tattymen' who scoured our streets giving out that distinctive cry for business. Sending all of us kids scurrying back home to pester, cadge and sometimes even steal arms-full of rags from our mothers.

To offer them eagerly in exchange for a colouring book, a stick of chalk perhaps, or maybe a balloon. Or then again, pegs or donkey stone for your mother to use. Cheap gifts for you to dash back home with excitedly, as though they were samples from some Arabian treasure chest.

Prizes kept within a hessian sack into which he would plunge his arm as you stood behind him expectantly, agog at the thought of what your reward might be.

Booty in return for the unwanted, or the worn out.

Household rejects which he would pile upon a cart already laden with everything from old bedsteads to baggy bloomers, all of it to be later sorted out and sifted through and sold off again to some mysterious collector of this unwanted flotsam, a Fagin who (to our childish minds anyway) lived in this huge Victorian warehouse somewhere beyond the Wicker Arches and spent all of his days rubbing grubby hands over a growing mountain of busted boots, bike wheels, worn out palliasses and bag upon bag of rags which his agents had dutifully delivered to him by way of us.

The soft sod, or so we thought. Fancy giving us something new for that rubbish!

Now, much later, I miss seeing them. Miss those painted little carts which they used, with that gold coloured piping running along the length of the shafts to break up the solid red or blue. I miss seeing the tailboard with the full sacks hanging from it, almost obliterating the elaborate scroll declaring the owner's name and that he was a *general dealer*.

I miss hearing hooves on the cobblestones and the occasional treat of seeing sparks fly as a metal shoe caught an uneven part of the lumpy surface.

3 Any Old Rags?

Ben Bradley was making clogs when he was photographed in 1971, and even as this gentle craftsman tapped usefully away at his last, amongst Star revolving heels, Blakey's and real leather laces, across the world in Woomera scientists were regularly testing atomic bombs. A moment of sanity in a mad world.

And I miss seeing the patient, usually dejected-looking pony move on or stop at its masters' commands of *yup* or *yo*, often shouted from many doors away as he searched for business down each entry and backyard. Cupping one hand to his mouth and regularly repeating his loud cry of *Ennyoldraaaaags*, so that we ran to respond, making those on the night shift curse for the disturbance.

Free enterprise at its best, its most colourful, most charismatic, and nowt at all to do with politics.

Tommy Nesbit was our Ragman, had been for donkey's years down there in Salmon Pastures. Long before any of us were born. He was part of the place was Tommy, just like the soot. A fixture, a natural part of the scene, not just a collector of rags or someone to take the junk away, but one of us.

He drank in the *Dog and Duck*, swept chimneys, cobbled shoes and replaced clog irons. He wallpapered for the old 'uns, and fetched their medicines, and he was *always* asked to attend church weddings, just for luck.

He used his cart time and again to shift furniture when a wardrobe or another large item was bought or sold. He even did complete flits for those who couldn't or wouldn't pay for a proper van.

In short, he was indispensible, inthat his usefulness relieved so many worries or expense. And all that he asked for in return was our rags and our rubbish.

I remember how his versatility even stretched to providing music by way of playing the old 'knick knacks', usually at Christmas or on those special occasions like wedding parties or anniversaries, you know, times when everyone drinks too much and gets merry or sloppy and succumbs to that daft urge to tap feet and sing well-loved songs. That's when he'd be called upon in the pub to demonstrate the artistic side of his nature by way of those whirling pieces of smooth ivory. Whipping them one-handed around his head and body, bending and straightening himself whilst all the time maintaining the furious rate of clicks and clacks which the bones made on contact with each other, creating a rhythm your toes couldn't resist.

Believe me, Bill Bailey never had a more enthusiastic plea for his return than that punched out by our Tommy, staccato style, with everyone else in the place banging their feet and roaring out the words. The essence of simple enjoyment, courtesy of Tommy the Ragman.

And I remember his black and white pony too.

The one all of us kids fantasised about pinching from him, to saddle and ride in a wild pursuit of the outlaws who'd just robbed the bank. Or to chase off savage Indians besieging that circle of wagons trying to make it to California. Imaginary whirlwinds with a six gun in each hand, just like all those celluloid cowboy heroes of ours did every Saturday afternoon at the pictures as we cheered and dipped into bags of Kali powder.

But we never did, pinch his horse I mean. To be honest, I was frightened to bloody death of it, really. It only had to shake its head and snort and I was off like the clappers. The only time I ever found enough bottle to reach out and stroke it's neck was when it had its nose-bag on at feeding time. And when it pee'd, Jesus, it was like the canal overflowing. Still, that's what dreams are made of, and we enjoyed them.

There must be thousands like me still around, who can recall the likes of Tommy Nesbit, and stir up humorous recollections of his kind. My favourite is of the time when he answered our gang's prayers by furnishing us with a brand new spanking white tennis ball. Beautiful it was, virginal in a world of eager feet. Not like the bald and usually punctured old rubber relics that we normally made do with. Trying to play football with them was the equivalent of juggling with jelly, and just as easy.

We never had a proper 'casey', so every time anyone trod on ours we had to stand about for ten minutes while the flaming air got back inside it to make it worth kicking again. And any that we had were no good for cricket either. I mean, it was sickening going to all the trouble of chalking up a set of wickets on the big wall opposite where we lived, getting Herbert Lee's dad to carve us a rough bat out of an orange box lid, go through all those noisy arguments of who'd have the first innings, and then watch in abject disgust as the first delivery hit the floor in front of the batsman and just lay there, dead, useless, or to coin a favourite expression of the time, flat as a fart. So, seeing as lily-white new tennis balls were about as common in 1947 as a bunch of grapes, you can imagine our unbridled joy at being presented for once with the means by which to enjoy these games to the full.

We had Pete Fairfax to thank for it. Him being the one to provide us with this good fortune by bringing along the apparently new black and white check ladies coat to offer Tommy that day. The rest of us had simply gaped open-mouthed at him, basically because, knowing his mum and how she used to sit around their house all the time clad in her dirty overalls from her job in the foundry at Firth Brown's, wearing a coat like that didn't fit in with her sartorial habits at all.

I remember Pete once telling us that the only time she ever took her flowered turban off was once a week when she went to Attercliffe slipper baths. And that was only because they were strict about it. Yet there he was, trading-in a garment which his mam would have readily forgone any time in favour of twenty *Capstan Full Strength*.

Overalls yes, but smart top coats? . . . Give over, not unless Firth Brown's issued them.

'Wheer did tha get that coat from?' we'd asked him as he gleefully spun the immaculate sphere over in his hands, gloating at it.

'It were in our yard, laid on one o' t' bins,' he'd muttered back, as though such trivia was hardly worth a mention.

'Whose bin?' we persisted, beginning to feel more than a little uneasy at all of this.

'T' one on t'end,' was all he said.

'Well who's is that?' We all wanted to know, but he made us wait for a bit by throwing the ball against the wall a few times and catching it one handed.

'Must 'ave been her's, Ria's,' he finally said.

'Ria Thorpe?!?!' we all chorused, moving half-a-yard away from him as though to absolve ourselves from any involvement.

'She'll go barmy when she finds out tha's pinched her coat and gen it t'ragman,' Harry Owen chortled, glad that for once it wasn't him who had done summat daft, yet unable to penetrate Pete's nonchalance.

'Tha'd better get it back,' I told him. The thought of Ria hunting us down terrified us lot, seeing as every time she spoke, huge cascades of saliva hit you full frontal. Believe me, the thought of Ria coming after us was enough to overcome any desire we might have had in sharing the spoils, and at that point Pete began to show the first glimmer of awareness of what he had done.

'She can't 'ave wanted it? Can she? I mean, why leave it on their bin? Eh? That means she's thrown it out, dun't it? That's what bins are theer for, innit? Aw c'mon, let's gerron wi' t'game.' And with a false air of bravado, he tried to get us to join in.

Only we didn't, or give him the re-assurance that he sought. I'm afraid we were all too familiar with the fact that Ria wasn't the sort to get quietly upset to be conned by Pete's assurances about there being nowt to worry about. We knew different. Ria could drown you if she put her mind to it.

'Are yer gunna play or what?' he'd snapped, growing frustrated at our refusals to tap the ball back each time that he sent it our way.

'Not me,' I said, 'if I were thee I'd find Tommy an' gi' him that ball back. Tell him tha's made a mistake an' tha wants that coat back. Tell him tha'rt in a lot o' trouble o'er it . . . go on, afore she comes after us.'

'I don't know where he is now, do I?' he protested.

'Find him then,' I snapped, losing patience and anxious for him to make a move, adding, 'we'll all cop it if . . .', then froze in horror at the sight of Ria turning into our little blank end, accompanied by old Ben Palmer carrying his long ladder which he kept on their entry wall due to him being a fire warden during the war.

'Jesus,' Pete groaned loudly. 'She's here.' And he ran down to the other end, to where the railings separated us from the canal bank, with the rest of us on his heels.

I still remember the furious argument which ensued between us all as we hid beside that stretch of oil-streaked dirty brown waterway. Much as we all desired that ball and the pleasure it could have brought, the thought of having to take the can back for Ria's coat finishing up on Tommy's cart overruled anyone's willingness to accept ownership of it. That's why, when Pete threw it to me I immediately tossed it to Harry Owen. And he broke all delivery records by slinging it straight back to Pete. And so it went on. To me, to Harry, to Sammy Gregory to Harry again, back to me and on to Pete via Herbert Lee.

A criss-cross, mish-mash, pass-the-parcel type of game without the benefit of anyone enjoying it or wanting to win. Until the inevitable happened, with Harry twisting away as Sammy lobbed it to him and the ball fell with a sickening plop into the filthy canal, leaving us all horrified at knowing that Tommy would never now accept it back even if we found him.

It was Harry's dad who found us. He knew where we'd be, and that his son would be with us, and came straight to the point.

'Does tha know owt abaht Ria Thorpe's best coat going missing?' he'd growled at his terrified lad as he half slid down the bank to join us.

'Arr, he did it,' Harry blubbered out straight away, pointing at Pete and beginning to cry before his dad even began to unfasten his belt.

Mr Owen then switched his fierce glare to take in the now white-faced culprit.

'What's tha done wi' it Lad?'

'He's gen it to Tommy Nesbit . . . for a tennis ball,' Harry had bawled out, not giving Pete a chance and getting a withering look back for his trouble.

'Christ Almighty!' said his dad, registering the kind of disgust which he usually reserved for his tax stoppages. 'What made thee do that?'

'I didn't know!' Pete had protested back loudly, spreading his hands in ignorance. 'It were on their bin, I though she'd thrown it out! Is she looking for it?'

'Not half as much as she's looking for thee,' he was told curtly.

Then, jerking his thumb at his weeping son, he sent him scuttling up the bank, leaving the rest of us

casting nervous glances at each other about his next move.

'She'd only left it theer for a few minutes while she fetched old Palmer to get through bedroom window 'cos she'd locked her sen out,' he told us coldly. 'Comes back and theer it were, gone! Do you lot know she's had that coat laid away eight months in Banners till she'd saved enough coupons up? Eh?' directing the last bit at Pete before carrying on, 'Does tha know what tha's done lad? . . . Eh? After all o' that waiting and saving she's done, what 'appens? . . . Tha goes and gives it to a bleeding ragman don't tha . . . Eh?'

'Well? Don't just stand here like souse all of yer . . . get the sodding thing back. *Now!*'

'We can't Mr Owen,' I told him weakly.

'Why not?'

'Cos our Harry's let t'ball fall in t'canal . . . an' we can't get it,' I remember squeaking.

For a moment he'd just stood there giving me a long unblinking look. Then he'd spun on his heel to clamber the bank his lad had just shot up.

'*HARRY!*' he roared out, his hand moving automatically to the buckle barely visible beneath his ample beer belly. Poor old Harry Owen, raised on leather pie, and about to get another helping.

Anyway, Pete Fairfax shot off over the old iron bridge faster than Flash Gordon's rocket shouting summat about 'Stopping wi' me Aunty Beattie for a bit', leaving us three to it.

'He's a nice pillock in't he,' Sammy Gregory had snorted, watching the disappearing figure. 'Causes all o' this, then teks his hook!'

But I didn't hear any more. I was too busy shooting the other way.

I heard later that Ria had made Pete's mother go with her to search for Tommy after Harry's dad revealed the missing coat's fate. Whether it was out of sympathy (new coats then being at a premium, what with shortages and clothing coupons), or just to calm her down and so avoid having to ask for a Mae West collar, I don't know. I do know that the pair of 'em set off to scour Attercliffe for the ragcart in a frantic bid to right the situation. Luckily for us, they did, because I dread to think what the consequences would have been if Ria hadn't got her coat back.

Mind you, so the story goes, *they* were lucky too, because Tommy was apparently in the final stages of selling it to 'Tich' Ward who used to go all over our area in those days selling oatcakes and pikelets from a wicker basket, as the two women burst into the dram shop of the *Sportsman* on Attercliffe Common after seeing his cart tucked away down the side.

And little Tich was determined to have it, seeing as his missus was going spare about having to go out every Saturday night wearing an old black 'swagger' coat which, (in her words), made her look like, 'A chuffing tent on castors'.

Well, it was like D-Day all over again as Ria pounced to reclaim what was rightfully hers and Tich refusing to part. They reckon tables and chairs went flying as the pair of 'em dragged each other about with the coat between them and Tommy doing his best to mediate, as everyone else in the place hung onto their beer like grim death, until Tich finally conceded, on the grounds of not being able to maintain a solid hold and wipe his face at the same time. He left the triumphant Ria to barge out purple-faced from the effort, but with the precious garment clasped tightly to her chest.

And *nobody* would get near to it again.

Looking back on it now, I can laugh at the memories which it evokes. Of Tommy the ragman, who must have thought he'd hit the jackpot when it was offered. And Pete Fairfax who must have thought the same when he saw it laid across her bin. Unable to resist finding out what he'd get in exchange for it. Of the way that we'd all sought refuge down by the canal once the terrible truth emerged about its true ownership, and how poor old Harry Owen immediately capitulated at the first sight of his belt-happy dad. Then Pete deserting us to save his own hide and me and the others following suit, scattering like chaff to wait until it had gone dark before daring to creep back home. Explaining

my long absence by saying that I'd been helping Herbert Lee to build a new rabbit hutch in their kitchen, dreading that I should be asked if I knew anything about the afternoon's proceedings, and the sheer relief on hearing that she'd got it back.

Great days, and smashing memories, comfort in the knowledge that ragmen and other such things were part of our childhood and that motorised scrap dealers can never take their place. I believe that Tommy died sometime in the sixties, well after I had left the area.

By then, the final destruction of the old east end was firmly under way, flattening his hunting ground and removing the very source of his livelihood. Taking his houses and yards and hordes of kids in their patched trousers and pig-tails, like a pied piper using his call instead of a flute.

'*Ennyoldraaaags?*'

Not any more, Tommy, not any more.

A pair of typical scruffy-looking kids from the 1940s, looking every bit like the Bisto kids who were advertised everywhere in those days. In fact they are my younger brother and sister.

I WOULD THINK that the names of Emile Zatopek and Fanny Blankeskoen will most probably mean very little to anyone not old enough to remember the 1948 Olympic Games in London.

And that's not surprising really seeing as Emile, a Czech, sounds like one of those foreign film directors making his name in Hollywood. Whilst Fanny, a Dutch woman, carries the ring of a pioneer woman involved in that early suffragette movement.

Yet these two, at track events anyway, were the shining stars of those games. Between them they devastated the cream of the world's best runners of the time by taking medal after medal as the rest trailed in their wake.

Now I'm mentioning this because, on a personal note, these two were the first examples I recall which we as kids then could look upon as being truly great stars of international sport. And let me point out here to those who are used to seeing it almost every day of the week now that, what with the war and shortages etc., sport had never played a prominent part in our young lives. Not organised sport anyway.

Ours had always been a rough and ready or make do and mend approach to it you see. Usually played in the streets or on 'rec's' using old or makeshift equipment. Like coats and jumpers for goal posts, or wickets which were drawn in chalk on a wall. Whilst bases for playing rounders would be lamp posts and borrowed bin lids.

Naturally, such elementary markers always led to fierce arguments over the validity of a team's claim. I mean, how do you tell if the 'casey' had gone into the goal inside or over the coats if it doesn't bounce back like it would off a proper wooden post? Or whether the mark on the wall where the middle stump was showed absolute proof of the last delivery or was, as the batsman always claimed, just a mucky patch.

'Tha'rt out!' we would all yell, pointing to the disputed evidence, demanding his exit from the

4 Going for Gold

Before the days of marathons there used to be the annual *Star Walk*. On a damp Sunday morning in 1954, on the dot of ten o'clock, thirty-four competitors set off from what was then. called Coles Corner, at the bottom of Fargate. How things have changed!

crease.

'Ahm not, tha knows,' he'd say, determined not to accept it, 'dat mark were theer last week', and so on . . . ad infinitum.

Jesus, we seemed to spend twice as much time arguing than playing in those days.

But play we did, despite all of the shortcomings, and it wasn't without its laughs.

Like the way in which the school kept about two dozen worn out black 'pumps' in a sliding cupboard. And the way we all dived in a mad snatching free-for-all to get a pair which at least matched each other in size. And I always seemed to finish up wearing two odd 'uns, making it impossible for me to do the physical jerks properly due to one being that big that I kept jumping out of it, while the other one was that tight my toes were doubling under my foot. And I remember how one time they paired me off with this other kid in the three-legged race on sports day and I held him up that much that we finished up rolling on the floor hitting each other whilst somebody else won the race. And believe me, it's not easy fighting with your legs tied together, either.

Yet it hadn't been my fault, it was the stuff they gave us to wear. I mean they'd tied my left leg (which for once was wearing a slipper that fit) to his right. Which meant that we'd lost before we even flaming started, seeing as how my free leg, the one that you really need to give you some push, was lumbered with a pump big enough to keep three pair of rabbits in.

Well, it stands to sense that I couldn't go any more than three steps without the sodding thing whizzing off at all angles and us two having to leave the measured course to retrieve it before we could start again. I know they all went barmy at me, but honestly, how do you win? It was the same when we all made the long trek to a park in the big holidays to play football.

We'd take bread and dripping sandwiches and a Tizer bottle full of water so we could stay out all day and have a proper match. Then we'd argue for an hour over who was going to be on what side before

finally getting on with the game.

Eventually someone would shout that it was half time and we would then flop out to eat the stuff we had brought and pass the water around. And guess what, I can guarantee that by the time it was passed to me it was always full of lousy crumbs. Floating up and down as I shook the bottle to try and make 'em sink. And I'll tell you summat else, it's not easy trying to drink through clenched teeth. Try it sometime. Oh yes, I remember it well.

But, as I said, it was endemic of the times and it didn't stop us from trying to emulate those two who I mentioned at the start. Of course, there were other stars before them like footballers and boxers, but mostly they were only figments we saw on newsreels or read about. You never actually felt that they were real, only that they existed inside another dimension away from us.

I mean, everybody knew that Joe Davies was the world snooker champion, but how many actually saw him play?

Now, of course, what with blanket TV coverage and personal appearances etc., they are far more accessible to their fans. So the chance of watching or actually meeting your particular sporting god today is obviously much greater than then. You see, we didn't have all these new athletic stadiums or olympic size swimming pools on our doorstep then. The world didn't tune in each year to the Crucible either to watch Steve Davies win yet again. We had to simply *imagine* what these stars were like because sport in our time was on a much lower level of availability. Yet we loved it all the same.

I know that there were some who were keen enough to join amateur clubs such as the Hallamshire or Sheffield United Harriers, but for most of us anyway, school was really the only place where we could have the use of even the most basic of equipment. Or take part in anything even remotely conducted under the prevailing rules of the game.

And even that was strictly limited to weekly swimming lessons (if you'd been good) at ancient baths like the ones at Attercliffe or Sutherland Road, perhaps Corporation Street or Hillsborough or Park, or further afield there'd be Heeley or Upperthorpe and Glossop Road.

Swimming by numbers, boys down one side and girls down the other, in white-tiled cramped little places with tiny cubicles to change in three at a time, standing on wooden duckboards, cursing as your short trousers stuck to your wet legs.

Such memories, along with the excitement of playing for your school and the whole assembly giving you three cheers for being victorious, making you feel like one of those remote stars. Especially if you had scored the winning goal, hit the winning run or in the girls' case, out-jumped everyone else at netball.

That is the feeling which winning at sport can bring, that inner glow of achievement. Along with the satisfaction of knowing that others wish that it were them and not you getting the glory. And do we not, given half a chance, find it hard to resist pinching a share of someone else's? As I did once at school when a cousin of mine completed the Star Walk and I felt ten feet tall bragging to all the other kids about it.

It didn't matter that he hadn't come home in the first thirty, he'd done it. He'd faced a hard challenge and he hadn't failed. And I could share his triumph through kinship.

I can clearly remember standing outside of the *Pheasant Inn* at Sheffield Lane Top amongst the crowd trying to get a glimpse of him in the line of walkers struggling to make that long hard pull up the hill from Ecclesfield. Letting my impressionable young mind take in a scene which portrayed so many facets of human nature on show to me as these men fought out two different battles with themselves.

One . . . the leg numbing and character searching trial of the race itself, and

Two . . . wanting to be a winner.

Puzzled as to why they should punish themselves so by taking on such an unforced challenge. And

guessing that it could only be that they needed to know if they could do it. Seeking to be an Emile as they presented themselves for inspection. Going for gold.

No wonder the race is so popular with us all. No matter whether trying to do it, or like me, just an observer over the years. Because, from a sporting view alone, the course itself is almost three times the length of the Grand National. And just as cleverly (or should that be cruelly) constructed so as to make the participant dig very deep to find that vital element which separates those who accept its trial from others like me, who don't.

I can fully understand its attraction each Whitsuntide because it operates upon four winning principles.

One . . . it's a challenge.

Two . . . it's a race through the streets.

Three . . . it costs nowt to watch and

Four . . . it combines a hard test for those who seek to be a local hero as well as a platform for the less dedicated who would turn it into a treat.

That's why it draws thousands of us each year to witness and enjoy its gala atmosphere. To clap and cheer and laugh at and encourage all of those determined to entertain us by their effort.

The afficianado, fit and lean and finely tuned with his movements perfected to give maximum propulsion so that the speed of his feet touch the ground so often that you half suspect that he could be breaking the basic rule of 'heel and toe' by running. Oozing an almost arrogant self belief in his ability to walk faster than we ever could as he zooms past, hips wiggling and arms jerking in that peculiar style relevant to this most insular of sports. Accepting our applause as his just desserts for showing us the way that it should be done as his muscular legs take the hills without flagging. Making those of us who only watch conscious of the omnipresent desire to win being paraded before us. Even by a silly walk. To beat everyone else and be the best. To be Einstein or Hercules, or better still for me, a pools winner.

Then there are the dreamers. Most of them ample bodied delusives struggling to keep in the race despite the mountainous evidence of excessive beer and bolted food being prominently displayed above and below straining vests and shorts.

Like an egg on legs as someone once described them as, with profuse sweat soaking their alarmed looking features, they cast continual backward glances. Reassuring themselves all the time that others were still behind.

Dreading the hills or of not at least making it as far as the point where family and mates were waiting to cheer them to the skies. Blindly ignoring, or perhaps suppressing, the truth of their non-existent hope of ever getting anywhere near to winning as they put on forced beams for their public.

Shaking a defiant fist before them in response to the encouragement coming their way.

'Go on our kid . . . it's all down hill now.' Or:

'Ah bet tha could sup a pint now couldn't tha me old luv? Shall I 'ave one for thee . . ?' Or:

'How's thi feet pal? Can tha still feel 'em? Eh? It's a good job tha can, innit, cos tha can't bleeding see 'em wi' a belly like thine . . . ha ha ha!' Or, the most hurtful one of all:

'Don't give up now, go on, keep going, tha'rt only an hour behind him at t'front'.

A far cry from the 'oh, well played sir' mutterings at that most English of institutions called Lords, I know, but then, what do you expect from the lower classes, especially when they're having fun?

Ours was an encouragement based on friendly ridicule, and that in itself very often acted as the spur which drove the recipient of it on to prove us wrong.

And if it didn't and we were proved to be right with such comments, well, where's the harm? We were helping him to find his limits, as these sort were doing that day. Martyrs to their own lack of preparation and the crowd's delight in telling them.

And finally, the foolish. The chorus line without which no show can be complete. The backstage wallahs whose names never get a mention on the billings out front. Making up the numbers so that the whole procedure has more atmosphere and variety. We had applauded the stars and encouraged the supporting acts, now bring on the clowns.

Like the six-foot-two-inch tall exhibitionist mincing along in sexy black stockings and suspenders stretched tightly over heavy thighs. Topping it off with a skirt hard pressed to cover his bum and a polka-dot, low-cut, balloon-filled blouse which fails to hide the forest of chest hair peeking out above his 'bumps'. Completing the ludicrous ensemble with exaggerated make up and a black patent handbag to which is attached a bold 30/- sign as he swings it provocatively towards grasping male hands.

In all probability a dumper truck driver on rough building sites by day, doing hard manual work yet who, given the public chance, feels this need to project his image thus. To tease and tempt the watching men with winks and pouts and thrusts of the balloons towards their grinning features. And they in turn responding to his game, with forced laughs and lewd grabs at his artificial temptations. Unable to totally resist feeling an urge to molest him as he passes close by them, challenging their manliness with his eyes and body movements.

So that some can't resist and stick out their hand to squeeze the toy balloons, ignoring his tattooed arms to ogle at his stocking tops. And I feel a mixture of amusement and embarrassment at this public display of weakness as the 'tart' leaves us and goes on his way with the race. No doubt enjoying every moment to come from those lining the route further on, awaiting their treat. Leaving us to savour the next tit-bit on this mixed menu of characters who give up their day to entertain us.

The old age pensioner.

I watch him and feel concern for his well-being as his little stooping frame approaches us. Trying hard not to laugh at his walk which is more of a painful limp than anything else due to him only putting the toes of one foot to the ground. Looking like a dog with a hurt paw.

His legs, or what bit that you can see of them, are ancient and full of bulging varicose veins as they protrude from beneath a voluminous pair of football shorts which stretch to reach below his knees, making it appear to us that his frail trunk reaches that far and that he hasn't brought his thighs with him today.

And we laugh in delight as he passes and we see the large cardboard sign pinned to his shirt back reading: 'Running in, please pass'. Laughing again as he gives us a toothless grin and answers with an obvious sense of triumph when someone questions his sanity at undertaking such a gruelling test that the alternative he had faced in not doing this would have been to 'Tek our old lass and her mother to Skeggy for t'day'.

And who are we to question his choice? Or that of all the others who followed him in a similar vein. For they are the icing on the cake, the light relief which enhances the overwhole taste. And the cherry on the top lies in the way in which the fun they gain in being a part of the day rubs off onto us. And I ask myself who is the bigger fool, they for doing it or us for not joining in.

My hope now is that this long tradition of working class sport will not be pushed aside in the new Sheffield which is emerging. Submerged beneath the concrete pillars of these multi-million pound emporiums which will no doubt turn us into a more discerning audience. For we are about to be spoiled by the world's top athlete's and swimmers and gymnasts, plying their trades before our astonished gaze in designer wear sport which is light years removed from ours as kids. We will sit in their magnificent workshops in covered comfort soaking in a kaleidoscope of colour and excitement being paraded for our benefit and wonder how in hell we ever put up with the cold and wet and uncomfortable conditions which had always been a part of sport before. And I have no doubt that we will revel in such things as we drink in their highly organised entertainment and applaud their efforts to please us. Just as we did for the Star Walk in earlier and poorer times.

And as we do I think that I will allow my thoughts to drift back to those days when we piled our coats on the ground. Letting them remind me of the time when Sammy Gregory sawed nine inches off his mother's brush handle to make us a new bat to play rounders with. Or the time when snotty Pete Fairfax lost us a relay race at swimming when we took on Southey Green school and he had to try and do the breast stroke and hold his trunks up at the same time when the ancient elastic in them broke yet again. And I'll smile at such things and be glad that I've known them. Sport in Sheffield before the days of the Don Valley Stadium.

So that when they are showing off with their state of the art PA systems and giant TV screens giving us instant and slow motion playbacks of these sporting titans, or they over-awe us by measuring speed in microseconds I will acknowledge the science they have brought to it. But if and when some four-foot-six high little Japanese kid brings the multitude to its feet by scoring maximum points after completing fifteen triple somersaults at the end of his display on the parallel bars, you will excuse me if I say to myself 'yes . . . yer clever little sod. I'd like to see thi do that and land on t'cobbles like we did.'

Then, purely from spite, I'll knock him a point off on my card for having it easy.

A puzzled group inspects a line of Anderson air-raid shelters being dug into spare ground behind their houses. Many of these simple corrugated iron arches still exist, banked around with soil or even a modest rock garden that once helped withstand bomb blast. Our shelter had two wooden bunks with sacking strips for mattresses and a duckboard to keep your feet off the frequently rain-sodden earth floor.

The disruption of domestic life during the War was often a source of great fun for kids, who played on bombed sites away from adult eyes, and spied gleefully on couples as they tiptoed into their shelters on quiet nights.

ACCORDING TO LOCAL LEGEND, when the first German bomb fell on Sheffield in the blitz, Gus Fenwick was having a pint in the *Big Gun* pub down the Wicker Arches, and he was back at home crouching under their pot sink before they had time to drop the second.

Personally I don't believe it, because for one thing the distance between the two points is a good three-quarters of a mile, and secondly, German bombs (except for landmines which came down on parachutes) were not noted for their buoyancy once you let go of them.

Be that as it may, I can still go along with the vindictiveness of the story because, like everyone else who shared the neighbourhood with him, my liking of Gus was akin to my love of neck boils.

Gus lived on Washford Road, not far from us, on his own, save that is for this Jack Russell terrier which would go to almost suicidal lengths to bite anything having the temerity to come within range of its stubby little legs, and that included on various occasions Gus himself. Now, as you can imagine, not only did this bring the dog a certain amount of local notoriety, but also provided us with the regular spectacle of seeing the little bundle of fun doing somersaults over the cobbles as yet another boot-end propelled it away. Proof indeed of their painful aquaintance with its voracious mouth. Not that any of this made it change its ways, in fact I always held the unproven theory that the little sod actually *enjoyed* a good kicking, and that its unprovoked attacks were specifically designed so as to bring about what I can only surmise as being a 'peculiar' satisfaction in its sick philosophy towards the human limb.

Right or wrong, the pair of 'em enjoyed a level of popularity down there usually reserved for a lapsed pawn ticket, *ie,* nobody wanted to know.

Yet, Gus had only himself to blame for all of this. Because I never knew any other bloke whose general demeanor and sheer bad manners towards anyone coming into contact with him made himself a deliberate pariah as he did.

He *never* varied his approach or treatment of us, or showed the slightest sign of favouritism. From the smallest kid to the oldest woman he gave good cause to *all* of us to dislike and isolate him. And I actually believe that he enjoyed doing it too.

The shock and the tears and the anger were deliberately sought, and then when he went too far and found himself in danger of a physical response he would quickly hide behind the convenient medical shield with which his bad heart provided him .

Gus Fenwick was Sheffield's answer to Goebbels, that insidious little dwarf used by Hitler to frighten and demoralise us in the war. And frighten us he did. In fact, Gus scared the life out of me and the rest of our gang when we were nowt but kids, to such a degree that *his* was the only house given absolute immunity from any pranks, collections and carol singing at Christmas by all save the foolhardy or the unknowing, and the likes of Harry Owen.

Good old 'I'll do it' Harry Owen, the world's first living brain transplant donor. Fearless, nerveless, unaware, going around with this permanent happy look of dis-orientation upon his moon-like features. So unco-ordinated that he couldn't walk and chew bubble gum at the same time.

Having long relinquished any pretensions of mental equality with the rest of us, Harry Owen concentrated upon the one thing he was better at, that is doing the things which we daren't do such as taking liberties with people like Gus and the beast which he kept as a pet. Perhaps that's why he drew the short straw on the one and only occasion that we dared to play the old and popular rope trick on the old varmint.

Now to say that it all went wrong is the equivalent in crassness to the captain of the *Titanic* asking where all the water was coming from. So let's just say that as a failure it was a complete success.

Thanks to Harry.

You see, the rope trick consisted of tying a length to the handle of one of the outside toilet doors across the yard and fastening the spare end to the handle of the chosen victim's back door facing it, so that when it was done you then hammered loudly on the back door, which was now unopenable. You then ran like hell to hide on top of the lavs, or behind the bins or in a dark corner, sharing the reward of scared mirth which we all derived from the efforts of those within to get out. And believe me, the risk of that was ever present, because you never knew when some member of the afflicted family would come steaming down that entry (having charged out through the front) spitting rivets in their determination to get you. That was the *real* test, the measure of how long your nerve could hold before you cracked and started legging it.

Harry's nerve, or lack of comprehension of what it entailed in terms of pain should you be caught, was always stronger than ours, hence the Gus Fenwick contract.

Anyway, as I said, it all went wrong. Not that it was *all* of Harry's fault. More a case of circumstances that the irrascible Gus should be perched upon the cold pot inside the lavvy at the exact moment that our chosen commando began to clumsily initiate the operation. Then again, how the hell do you legislate for the unique, if not idiosynchratic habit of someone who actually took his dog with him to perform what is to most of us a very private function?

This habit was unknown to us, and certainly unheard of to the natives, so perhaps that's why it was so anti-social to the rest of us. I mean it's quite possible for a dog to take deep offence at such blatant disregard for its finer feelings just as we might do. And it would be understandable, because although it was common to be wary of seeing a rat, most of us made do with a bit of candle in a jam jar. Some even took a poker along, just in case, but a dog? In such a confined space?

I mean, where did it sit? On his knees? And if it did I can't imagine that being owt like comfortable for either of 'em. One thing's for sure, it made our young and impressionable minds boggle at the

mental visions which it threw up once we learnt of the unusual Fenwick preference.

But enough of that, and back to dear old barmy Harry doing the honours on the outside of the said khazi, with Gus unbeknown to him and us doing 'em on the in.

Then all bloody hell broke loose in that yard. The lavvy door whipped open, there was this white flash and our lad suddenly found himself transfixed by the sight and sound and feel of a manic dog, now hanging down the front of his body with its teeth unbreakably locked into his tatty jumper, making at the same time all of those funny gurgling noises which meant that it was enjoying itself and which also put the wind up bitches on heat. Well, the next thing that we saw from our various hiding places was the figure of Gus emerge, clutching his unfastened trousers with one hand whilst using the other to grab a handful of our hero's hair, demanding in that pleasant guttural way of his, explanations of Harry's intent, viz-a-viz, after dark, length of rope, his back yard, during necessary ablutions. The fact that he totally ignored the dog suspended three-foot above the yard attached to Harry, and that he was stretching the lad's hair to its root-tugging limit, only went towards illustrating his determination to get some answers from the petrified culprit. Typically, we didn't deter him one iota from pursuing it.

Now, there is no doubt that at that point Gus held all the aces. We were in the wrong and he was in the right. Harry was taken prisoner while the rest of us lay quaking in fear lest he should crack and give us away. What to do? Apply the first principle of all failed pranks and run for it? Every man for himself? Personally . . . yes, leaving Harry to the whims of the half-dressed Gus and his newly-aquired bosom pal which now hung down him like a white silk scarf. But luckily for Harry and the presence amongst us that night of Sammy Gregory, the toughest kid in our school, no.

All that I remember seeing was Sammy's stocky figure suddenly appearing behind Gus to scoop up

TRAVEL
BY
S.U.T.
TO
SKEGNESS
AND
MABLETHORPE

DEPART
SHEFFIELD
8-15

RETURN
FARE
23/3

SATURDAYS
& SUNDAYS
26/3

the discarded rope and give the old varmint a great whack with it across the swathe of bare flesh showing twixt the sagging top of his trousers and the bottom of his collarless shirt, the lap of which was tangled up inside the grip that he had on his trouser front. Christ, did he jump! He let go of Harry, whipped around to see Sammy doing an Olympic jump back up the wall, realised that he had let go of the culprit and spun back again. Harry by this time had staggered back a little so that Gus's desperate grab missed him and sank instead into the dog's back, and to top it all his flaming trousers fell down altogether.

Well, there we were, wide-eyed and frightened to death, with Harry wailing aloud about the dog attached to his jam infested jumper with Gus still trying to maintain contact via the now horizontal beast's stretched skin, whilst desperately trying to

This 1940 photograph shows the first parade of a unit of the Home Guard on Victoria Station approach. Some have plainly seen better days and may have used the penny lift from the Wicker to save climbing the flight of steps.

25

retrieve his errant kecks.

'Run!' I remember shouting out to Harry, 'Run, mek him let go of thee'.

And the others joined in, Pete Fairfax and Herbert Lee and Sammy. Voices emerging from dark places to confuse Gus and encourage our mate.

'Run,' we kept on calling, until finally Harry responded and began to pull away, extending the limpet between him and Gus so that the noises coming from its throat began to change, rising an octave to a more puzzled and higher pitch. A sort of questioning whimper as its master's digging fingers took it one way and its own unforgiving teeth took it another. Until the ridiculous connection broke, sending our lad tumbling backwards with the dog still attached, and Gus to fall forward onto the asphalt with his scrawny legs clearly visible amongst the untidy heap.

How Harry ran and followed us that night still carrying the dog I will never know, but he did.

Criss-crossing those dark inter-woven streets supporting the unwanted load to him with half of his tatty jumper still inside its mouth and despite his tearful pleas for relief.

Never stopping until we were safely back in Salmon Pastures again and those familiar hollows on the weed-infested canal bank, to fall down into a heap on each other laughing in relief, letting the tension dissolve itself uncontrollably at the sheer ludicrousness of what we had just witnessed.

At Harry crying in frustrated anger at the glassy-eyed appendage he'd just aquired and of Gus squirming around the cold surface, undignified in his struggles to preserve propriety and at the same time punish the prankster. And failing in both. At the splendid excitement of it all going wrong and of getting away with it, and of the marvellous tale we would have to tell in class next day with all the envy that it would create amongst those of lesser daring. And best of all, that it had been perpetrated upon the dreaded Gus. The one that we *all* wanted to hurt.

Eventually that night we did free Harry. Herbert Lee did it by dashing home to fetch the remains of a quarter bag of aniseed balls he had left. Gingerly wafting the bag beneath the dog's nose (or rather the bit you could see inside Harry's jumper) so that the aroma of them did what no amount of pleas and punches to its rock like head could do, and Herbert, like a skilled poacher, lured it until it could resist no more. Releasing its exhausted victim to dive for the morsel offered. To snap and crunch the prize, leaving Harry to scrabble away up the bank tearfully, surveying his ravaged middle and predicting what his mam would do later on because of it.

That was when we decided to make our revenge complete upon the hated enemy. We would hit him where he would really feel it, make his isolation even more acute by losing the dog. That *would* hurt him, much more than being shunned or glared at everywhere he went, it would bring home to him that now he was *really* on his own, and let's see if he liked that.

We would lose the dreaded dog far away beyond Norfolk Bridge to our delight and his dismay. Amongst the labyrinth of Firth Brown's steelworks down Carlisle Street, never to surface again from that mass of furnaces and press-shops and yards. To disappear forever into the noisy hell which it deserved, or so we thought.

So we did it. Ball after ball of the canine drug was strategically placed by Herbert and greedily snapped up as we slowly enacted the deliberate abduction. Carefully rationing the lure, so as to not run out until we were halfway down that high-walled canyon and certain that the gate we chose was far enough away to jettison the four-legged junkie.

And with the rest of us plaguing him with whispered encouragement, Herbert tempted it inside the yard. Scared should a works 'bobby' suddenly appear, yet determined to see the act through.

We had urged him further and further within, to where an open door lay beyond which, who knows what?

Then the final act as he emptied the two remaining balls into his hand, dropping the sweet-smelling bag for the dog to frantically tear apart in its craving. The hopeful look in its eyes as Herbert rattled them above it, and its rush to follow as he flung them as far as he could inside the works. Slamming the door shut behind it before haring after us in our headlong rush to leave.

I don't think that I have run as fast as that ever again, not as I did down Carlisle Street that night. Silently flying away so that no single noise would give it any idea of direction should it escape.

Silent, yet elated at what we had just done, racing for all we were worth, back towards familiar surroundings and growing more bolder as no sight or sound of the beast made itself known to us. Cockiness and a touch of arrogance as we reached Norfolk Bridge again and the outer marker of 'our end'. The beginnings of laughing responses between us as fear gave way and hearts slowed down again, confidence returning. Each running step a nail in the coffin of the dog which we had just

Sheffield's Corporation tramcars gave a us service second-to-none, but they had one bad habit. Trams could turn round almost anywhere, for all the driver had to do was to stop and take his seat to the back of the tram and start driving in the opposite direction.

The Haymarket entrance to Norfolk Market Hall showing Bunney's clothes shop and Inman's the grocer. Tylers tobacconist shop on the corner is where thousands of women queued in the War for hours, often for just one packet of cigarettes.

metaphorically buried.

Charging victoriously down Salmon Pastures past closed curtains, behind which neighbours read papers, listned to the wireless, pegged rugs, did jigsaws and a thousand other things which filled long nights before television. Unaware of the blow that we had just struck for them, or so we thought, as we whooped and laughed and shinned up gas lamps to swing on the arms or kicked cans noisily over the cobbles in our victory dance. The euphoria of success within us. The satisfaction of winning.

But, oh, the sickening feeling which followed it

the next day upon finding that it had all been in vain. All for nowt. All the effort and the planning and the risks blown away in a useless gale as we discovered that the animal was back, safe and sound and just as dedicatedly vicious as before. Re-united with its detestable owner and free to terrorise us once again. The disbelief at how fate could have led us to the very gate amongst all the host of gates down there where the gate 'bobby' just happened to be related by marriage to Gus, and recognising the dog had brought it back to us after keeping it safe all night.

Of Harry Owen's dad being visited by the whining Gus to complain and of Harry's backside being introduced yet again to that broad leather belt which *all* fathers wore then.

And of it robbing us of glory which we had all expected to receive at school and on the streets when our campaign became known. One that we had so much wanted to brag about.

It was a lesson to us all that mischief brings its own punishment, and that claiming premature victory is a game for fools. That the Gusses of this world are sent to teach us a lesson, in that bad behaviour rebounds eventually upon its own perpetrator. And that no real satisfaction can come of it. In his case it brought him isolation and rejection. In ours, guilt and the big belt. I am glad now, in retrospect, that our's was the latter. The belt hurt for a while then faded, and feeling guilty soon wears off when you're back playing with your laughing and squabbling pals. To being an accepted part of the gang and the street and the community. To *doing* things with others instead of imposing on yourself a life of chosen isolation.

This was what Gus chose to do, and he paid the price of it. Wherever he is now I hope that he found a way to break that terrible outlook. In whatever form it may have come, because no-one deserves to spend the whole of their life in such a cruel and bitter atmosphere such as he endured. I hope he did, change I mean, because despite our views of him in those times, I still remember him. I wonder if he would still remember us?

T HE NEXT TIME that you hear anyone praising Sheffield for its steel, be sure to tell them it was the ale that did it. Pints and gallons and oceans of the stuff. Filling tall pots with its golden essence and wearing a crown of moving froth, slaking parched throats with a cooling relief whilst replacing the torrents of sweat which poured from those defying Danté's heat. Steelworkers in their clogs and aprons, with caps pulled forward providing scant protection for the face, the end of a sweat towel gripped tightly inside scorched mouths and eyes reduced to protesting slits behind dark glasses as they peered into the white and yellow glare of roaring furnaces which extracted a burning price from them, watched over from on high by crane drivers, anxiously awaiting the seering upward rush of the blast as they delicately positioned massive ladles ready to receive the teeming of the molten steam which would pour forth once tapped.

Giving birth to an element which would fashion the billet, from which would come the bar, or the plate or the strip, or castings for giant forgings which would in turn produce controlled power in many forms. Terrifying forces of industrial nature coaxed into obedience by those puny in relation to its power. And all sustained by ale.

It was amongst such men that we grew up. Fathers and brothers and uncles and cousins. Watching as they went, grey-faced, on shifts with their mashing cans and 'snap' packed into ex-army shoulder bags. Travelling on the top decks of trams swathed in a cloying fog of Woodbine smoke, heads buried deep inside the *Daily Herald* or the *Sporting Life* as their bodies jerked and rolled to the swaying of the clanging transport.

Often succumbing after a long night-shift into an aching sleep as the atmosphere and movement overcame them, weary from the labour and limbs shivering in the cold morning air away from the heat.

Sheaf Street in 1960, with a tram driver adjusting his tramcar and a topical Guinness advert on the wall behind. You couldn't stand in the middle of the road doing that sort of thing nowadays, but life was slower and there were far fewer vehicles on the roads then.

Those were men who *needed* beer. They needed to replace those body fluids that sweated out of them while they worked, and to some extent they needed a liquid crutch which helped them through such shifts and obliterated their senses over a weekend as they waited for it all to begin again.

My father did it, as thousands before him had, and I did it too, although my own contribution was to come much later and in the cooler regions of strip rolling. Playing our part in the manly tradition demanded by Sheffield's finest ambassador, maintaining the anachronistic macho image created by others in a much earlier and harder time, unaware that time was fast running out for us, and that our seemingly impregnable world of steel would soon kneel to the foreign markets which we disdainfully supplied, and a way of life would end, taking the ridiculous machoism with it.

All of my childhood memories revolve around such scenes as these. Of men and their wives, drinking in pubs and clubs, with ample beer bellies partly covered by waistcoats, and best suit trousers held up by broad leather belts above brown shiny boots. Of flat caps on straight at opening time and at ninety degrees when they came out. Drinking endless pints until staggering forth at closing time, proving easy prey to crafty kids like me who had waited frozen stiff for them with a tatty Guy Fawkes effigy stuffed into a decrepit old pram, or gave them a poor rendering of *Away in a Manger* at Christmas time, which guaranteed to make their wives go 'aaah', sentimentality apparently wiping out the memory that perhaps only a few hours earlier we had been little sods for kicking a ball against their line of clean washing.

'Ere tha are, kid,' the man would say, anxious to impress his misty-eyed spouse that he had got feelings as he'd press a threepenny bit into our hands, then add with exaggerated solemnity as he swayed and slurred 'and don't thee go and waste it, will tha'.

This was sound advice which always struck me as being paradoxical in its content, seeing as how my benefactor had probably just blown a third of his week's earnings doing exactly what he was now warning me against.

But, in retrospect, I suppose it was wrong of us to deliberately play upon their drink-induced weaknesses. For pubs and clubs and ale were the great relief they sought from the grey confines of daily life.

Places where dads proved their allegiance to the male image, and mothers took meat sandwiches and pork pies on a Sunday night, in the confirmed belief that no one but no one could possibly sing *On Mother Kelly's Doorstep* properly without a mouthful of black 'dag'. For it was often the pinnacle of a woman's week to play hostess in such circumstances, even if it was far removed from the muted soirées presented on the far side of Endcliffe Park, and it has to be admitted that a bottle of milk stout would do little to enhance the silverware, or that big juicy pickled onions are the perfect complement to after dinner mints.

But what the hell, *they* enjoyed it.

And I recall how some preferred to drink at home by fetching it in from corner beer-offs. It would be measured carefully into large white or willow patterned jugs, to be savoured perhaps in the light of dancing reflections which a coal fire made on the shiny wood of a solid oak sideboard, or sipped between reading or knitting or listening to familiar voices on the wireless, ending the day with a drink.

From such lessons did we, as kids, observe and learn. For should you want a pup, or to go with your dad the next time that he went fishing on the Trent, you didn't bother him when he came home knackered from a night shift at English Steel. You applied the lesson of drink, and waited until he came home knackered from the ale-house instead.

That was when your odds of success were at their highest, when he flopped down into his chair and loosened his stiff collar, blowing out through flushed cheeks as he asked with tired eyes 'Are tha alreight, son?'

That's when you pounced.

And if you could get him to agree in front of your mam you'd got it made, 'cos he couldn't plead ignorance the following morning when his promises were brought home to him, and you knew that your tearful insistence would be backed up by her annoyed witness.

'Oh, aye, tha did,' she would jump in, as all women do, 'it's thi own fault for supping so much.'

Believe me, half of the mongrels and a million pairs of women's shoes would never have set foot on Attercliffe's streets were it not for the Saturday night sting. And if in later years we look back on such tactics and question their legitimacy at taking such advantage we can console ourselves with the knowledge that our fathers would have been just as devious with nowt in their pocket and gagging for a drink.

You see, beer went beyond the realms of a mere pleasure or relief for most of these men. It reached and became the euphoric day-dream of becoming a landlord themselves, from imagining the blessed gift of endless days and nights with unimpaired access to the addictive ambrosia, to wallowing in the enjoyable envy of all those who had to pay to share

your good fortune whilst continuing to do those arduous shifts, wishing they were you.

Which is exactly why Billy Whittaker set his stall out to become a landlord. It hadn't taken him long into his working life (covering a multitude of manual jobs) to realise that pulling pints was infinitely better than pulling your guts out.

'Let them other chuffs do it if they want,' he'd snapped at his widowed mother as she had furiously demanded a reason for packing in yet another job. 'I know what I'm after'.

And being the single-minded sort, he'd gone flat out to get it. Now whether it was what he really wanted from life, or whether the driving force was the prospect of being forever lumbered with what all the others were doing, is hard to tell. What I do know is that the initial reaction to him when he took over the *Dog and Duck* with his newly-aquired wife, Bella, was that if *she* was the price payable in attaining such a privileged position then a man was better off doing regular nights.

God, she was awful to look at. The sort of woman who doesn't improve no matter how much you supped. Her nose seemed to inhabit most of her

Pre-fabs (pre-fabricated homes) were put up after the War to replace homes damaged by bombing. For most people they were a revelation, for they came with fitted fridges, immersion heaters kitchens and all-night burning fires. My sister had a pre-fab on the Arbourthorne Estate, where all the roads were built by German prisoners of war. They wore chocolate brown boiler suits with yellow circles on the back, and were even allowed into town.

face, and she never smiled. Mind you, come to think of it, I doubt that her lips would have found a way past it if she'd tried.

As Gus Fenwick said as he unblinkingly surveyed the face for the first time, 'Christ, the last time I saw owt like that, Tommy Ward's elephant were pulling a wagon wi' it.'

'Can't tha ever say owt reight about anybody for once?' Curly Bradshaw spat out at him. The contempt in his voice fuelled by personal experience of the old varmint's acidic tongue.

'Course ah can,' Gus had sneered back, unabashed. 'Wi a conk like that, she can have both hands full and still scratch her arse, how's that?'

Curly had simply walked away.

Now it came to light after those first few days that she was the daughter of the publican that Billy had begun work for as a cellar-man in his first tenuous step on the ladder of his own personal goal. And you didn't have to be Einstein to realise that his ascent must have been speeded considerably by the father's connections within that obscure section of the brewery which could make his dream come true. At a price.

'Sod that!' Sam Duffy had snorted as Billy's sacrifice was discussed one night by the usuals, 'I'd rather work hard'. A declaration viewed by the others as being even more ludicrous than Bella's facial predicament.

Billy himself chose to ignore whatever he heard said about her, choosing instead to create the impression that keeping his pipes clean was of much greater importance, and I have little doubt that forced to choose between the flow of money and her embarrassment at what was openly said, his preference would have been treacherously obvious.

Legend has it that he only once re-acted in her favour. Well, not completely like, but sort of half way, and that was the night when she made the heinous mistake of removing Ria Thorpe's milk stout whilst it was still half full shortly after closing time. Now I'm old enough to remember when pubs still employed white-aproned waiters, and it is a fact that the two golden rules of waiting on were that you were always extremely careful not to short change, and to be always ultra cautious about removing glasses and bottles, simply because your fingers ran the distinct possibility of being badly mishapen should you err in either. In short, it made the punter get nasty, and when it turned out to be someone like Ria of the rampant spit you took your pick; apologise quickly and hope for the best, or put a diver's helmet on. But, on this occasion it wasn't just some obsequious waiter that Ria had rounded on. Oh no, it was big-nosed Bella, and Bella, pig sick of the treatment which she had endured from day one, was past caring about any watery risk she might be running.

So they went at it hammer and tongs, with everybody else quickly shoving their remaining ale under the table out of Ria's reach or covering it with a cap whilst poor old F . . . F . . . Freddie did his best to support his wife by pointing at the screaming Bella and stammering at Billy that 'She shun't . . . she shun't . . . she shun't . . .' It was left to Billy to mutter something about not having a week to spare just now, as he concentrated on trying to separate the two of them before hair started parting company with scalp. His demands (through screwed-up features as Ria turned on him) that Bella had been right in doing it seeing as how his licence could be in jeopardy, had the double effect of making Ria screech and spray even more effectively and everyone else swiftly switch from hiding their ale to quickly swallowing it before Bella could get to them as well.

Well, it was like queuing for Coalite on the Canal Wharf listening to these two going at it that night. I don't know who was more shocked by it all, Ria losing her habitual nightcap or Billy for thinking that being a landlord only entailed putting loadsamoney into the till. Not forgetting Bella, who by now had backed off two yards seeing as Ria had threatened to 'break thi bleeding fingers' had she not relinquished her grip upon the offending bottle.

Whatever, Billy must have done some quick

thinking, and I imagine it must have dawned on him that landlords who let wives or waiters clear tables too quickly after closing time ran the very real risk of finding themselves having very few tables to clear at all. In fact, had *that* kind of information leaked out into the general neighbourhood down there it would have spread faster and further than somebody's daughter announcing the dreaded words of 'Ah've got summat to tell yer, mam'. *And* it would have been received with about the same enthusiasm.

So, there's the pair of 'em with Ria gripping her bottle of stout tighter than Tessie O'Shea's knicker elastic and Billy doing his best to find a way out of it which won't ruin him. With everyone else in the place holding their breath, seeing as how the outcome would decide whether or not they would have to take their beer bellies elsewhere rather than have big-nosed Bella lurking over them at closing time.

It was quite a scene. What with the shouting and insulting and shoving and pushing between the two women and Billy trying to part them and Freddie going purple in the face trying his best to argue his wife's case and everybody else doing the St. Vitus Dance in their efforts to avoid the flying spray. Until finally Billy grabbed a tin tray from the bar, and banging it violently several times on a table, succeeded in making everybody break off.

'Jesus Christ,' he said, shaking his head in disbelief and scratching his head, 'I don't believe it! It's only half a' bottle of stout,' he went on, adopting a coaxing and hurt tone into his voice as he admonished the two participants of the row. 'I mean, anybody 'ud think it were a cartload o' nylons yer were scrapping o'er'.

'It's mine, paid for an' all!' Ria had spat out into his unprotected and unready face.

'Not after closing time it isn't!' Bella yelled back as Billy dragged the bottom of his shirt out to dry himself.

'*Look!*' he yelled, flapping his hands up and down in a calming motion, 'enough . . . alright?'

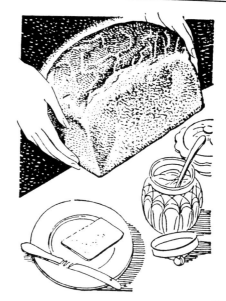

Once again, an uneasy calm descended on the place. Billy, spreading his hands and appealing to everyone in there, did his best to repair the situation.

'We don't want any of this now do we?' he whined, 'I mean, there in't no reason why we can't all be pals, I mean, bloody hell, that's what yer come in here for innit, to 'ave a good time like . . . drinking yer beer, that's why we like 'aving yer here, innit . . . *every* night,' addressing the last bit meaningfully at Bella.

Now, I've got to hand it to the lad because he almost succeeded in bringing a bit of sanity back into the room with his submission of how things had got out of hand, and then Freddie Thorpe went and spoiled it all.

'She shun't . . . she shun't 'ave,' he chimed in, pointing and glaring at the re-aroused Bella again.

Well, up it went again, and when she responded by saying that she'd got a budgie what could talk better than him, that brought the frightening Ria alive once more, and we were back to square one.

'Here . . . here . . . here!!' Billy screamed, dragging a handful of change out of his pocket, tearing the bottle from Ria and slamming the coins on the table.

'No more, does tha hear me? Eh? Tek thi money, go on, tek thi money back.'

Ria and Freddie stood there, lost for words. Well, you could say that Ria was.

'I mean it,' Billy had grated, shuffling the coins around and sorting out the tenpence she had paid. 'Tek thi money and go home, both on yer, *please*'.

A low murmur had gone around the place at that. I mean, what we had here was an event which didn't occur in most of their lifetimes, and when something momentous happens, whatever it is, it takes a while to sink in. To all the others watching, Billy was setting an unknown precedent amongst landlords which would go down forever in local history when people recalled the old days. Giving you your money back in a pub, and willingly at that by the actual landlord, somehow had to be wrong. There had to be a catch, a sting in the tail. He was going to bar 'em, they decided, silently. That was it, he was paying 'em off and the price was cheap compared to losing his licence. So Ria had paused, naturally, alternately looking at him and the proferred coins before her.

'Are yer throwing us out?' she asked, suspicious like.

'No,' he said, firmly.

'Are yer telling us not to come in any more?' she countered.

'No,' he snapped, causing all the others to catch their breath as he destroyed their theories of his motives.

'I'm telling yer,' he went on, 'that I don't want to see me customers done out of what they've paid for, that's all. So seeing as how yer didn't get time to finish yer drink, I'll give yer part of yer money back, that's fair, innit?'

And then he let his gaze wander all around the rest as he repeated the demand.

Ria had then picked up the money, and with a curt jerk of her head at the door to Freddie, had swept out triumphantly, leaving poor Bella to barge Billy aside as, with eyes blazing, she fled through the bar and up the stairs to their flat above, and the sound of things being banged and smashed up there filled the deathly silence that she had left below.

'Quite a performance in 'ere last night then,' Alf Skinner had quizzically remarked as he paid Billy for his pint the following night.

Billy had deposited his money safely in the till before answering. 'Between me and thee kid, it were a straight choice, her nose or,' jerking his thumb over his shoulder at the till, 'that going hungry, and if that's t' case, well, she'll 'ave to start wearing a gas-mask again, won't she'.

Alf had blown out slowly through puffed cheeks at such blatant preference.

'Know what?' he said to him quietly, 't' next time that I get any daft ideas about being a landlord I'll think about thee and go back to work'.

And so saying, he turned his back on the puzzled looking Billy.

7

A fiver on the nose

I HAVE ALWAYS known horse racing to be described as the sport of kings. A dual involvement between animal power and man's efforts to manipulate it. A world inhabited by the highest of society, along with those whose wealth enables them to indulge in attempting to influence nature by way of the selected breeding of bloodstock, forever pursuing the dream of creating an animal which will not only confirm their skill and knowledge of such matters by carrying their silks to glory in some great classic contest, but also afford them envious respect for the way in which such success will elevate their standing within that fraternity. Not to mention the shekels which will undoubtedly follow as others pay dearly for the privilege of drawing upon such qualities in their own efforts to better it, and so on *ad infinitum*.

And yet, although it is an insular club far removed from a working man's means, horse racing has always relied upon those unable to share such depth of involvement to make up the great crowds at Catterick. Or Epsom, Ascot or Newmarket and each and every other course which stages the spectacle.

For we are necessary in generating the emotive atmosphere which lifts and stirs their genetically engineered products. I mean, how can the joy of winning the Derby be wholly complete if it lacks the witness of the multitude roaring its approval?

I'll swear it was the feeling of sharing its exclusiveness, however fleetingly, as much as finding the winner which made its pull irresistable to most of the men that I watched as a lad, furtively slipping their bets to 'Fat' Burns, the bookie's runner down our way. He was the link, him and that special bag with the clock set into its neck. It was via him and his bag that a man could make or break his day, or his wages. Invariably leaving him not only pig sick at getting his form calculations wrong, but also pondering on how the hell he would placate his raving wife when he told her later that he was 'short' yet again.

Believe me, the sight of women waiting at the

Cambridge Street in the days when No Waiting signs had flip-over tops so that different sides of the road could be used on different days, and you could book second-house seats at the *Hippodrome* and then have a drink in *Nells* while you waited Then it was three hours of make-believe with Betty Hutton or Clark Gable in glorious technicolour, ending in a swaying tram ride back to grim reality. And all for less than ten bob!

works gates on pay day anxious to grab 'theirs' before Fats took his was usually a better race to watch than the Caesarawitch. Proof indeed that our love of the ponies entailed a mixture of emotions which could have graced many a stage, and in Rosie Crapper's case there was one time when she'd have given anything for it to open up and swallow her out of harm's way.

Now Rosie, you may recall, had a pair of ears that a vampire bat would have been chuffed to own. She missed nowt. They should have stood her on Beachy Head during the war and chucked radar away. And she repaid the angels for this gift by informing the rest of us as quickly as she could of all the gossip and tittle-tattle which her twin antennae picked up. Believe me, she wasn't lightly bestowed with the title of 'that bleeding pest in a turban' for nowt.

Anyway, there she is in old Doctor Hudson's waiting room one morning, concentrating full power into eavesdropping on what he is shouting down the phone in his surgery (despite the annoying distractions of coughs and sneezes and all the other strange noises one hears in such places) and picking out key words like 'Lincoln', and 'four-thirty, Saturday' and 'twenty quid' and what sounded like 'Padimore' or 'Palidor', all of them tantalising verbal segments of a jigsaw which her fertile mind desperately sought to connect, inducing her into the excited, and totally wrong conclusion that the old quack was in the process of investing a considerable sum of hard-to-come-by cash upon a nag.

Now, had she but known, or better still kept her big nose out of it, he was merely answering a call about a doctor called Paramore who had shared his days as a medical student before setting up a practice in Lincoln, and the four-thirty and twenty quid bit referred to the time and cost should he and his wife wish to say *au revoir* at the post-retirement dinner and dance being held for him. So, what we had in effect was an old deaf doctor roundly telling some tater over the phone what he thought about laying out that sort of 'dosh', and Nosey Rosie

thinking she was onto some inside information and dying to tell the world about it.

Well, all of our end anyway.

Now, you could say that with this in mind, and with the hindrance of what she had initially gone to see him about out of the way, she then made her way swiftly back to Salmon Pastures. Or you could put it as old Mrs Flynn did as Rosie zoomed past her as she came out of Banner's store, by saying that the 'fat sod was going faster than a week's bacon ration'.

Whatever, the fact remains that under any other circumstances Rosie's message would have assumed the same credibility as a pronouncement that all the pawn shops in Attercliffe were about to be nationalised.

But this was different. So different in fact that a little seed took root in most minds seeing as how if she *was* right and they chose to ignore her, they'd be cursing themselves for letting their usual disregard for what she said inflict a painful loss upon their pockets. And the fact that a horse called Parador *was* running at Lincoln that Saturday was enough to push most of them over the edge. So they backed it, in droves.

We had Curly Bradshaw from the corner shop splashing a fiver each way on it when he heard the odds of one hundred to six. And you could have put that down to being the equivalent to one of Christ's miracles seeing as how he could (to use Gus Fenwick's flowery style) 'skin a fart'.

And Sam Duffy. Grief, he couldn't keep a limb still when Edna told him about it. He got that excited about it that he completely missed the plate of meat and tater pie she put before him and shook the bottle of relish he was gripping straight into his mug of tea. And that, in our day, was sacrilegious.

Anyway, it got him to such an extent that after doing several careful calculations on what ten bob each way would bring in, he lost his head completely and promised to buy Edna new shoes out of the expected winnings.

'He's what?' Alf, their lodger, had gaped at her when she told him.

The *Grand Hotel* stood on Leopold Stret, and this is the back of it, seen from Barker's Pool. Its opulence was legendary, and all the big names who visited Sheffield stayed there, for it was handy for the *Playhouse, Hippodrome* and all the other theatres, as well as the City Centre generally. Many people will remember the Dive Bar underneath the hotel, which was a popular meeting place.

Today only Balm Green Gardens remains, whilst Cockaynes moved back to Snig Hill and then became Schofields, before disappearing completely in the early 1980s.

'Promised,' she'd giggled. 'Reckons he'll 'ave o'er eleven quid to come back, sez I can 'ave three of it for some new shoes.'

'I don't believe it . . . I just don't believe it.' Alf had laughed at her, shaking his head and pursing his lips. Then letting his face break into a mischeivous smile he urged her:

'Ask him for four . . . tell him that they cost more now cos they don't mek 'em wi' buttons up fronts any more.'

Well, it goes without any need from me to explain that the horse didn't fulfil their dreams. In retrospect I am being far too generous to the beast,

for it would be nearer the truth to say that if it had been one furlong further back at the finish then it could have taken part in the following race.

It was so out of its class that the jockey was heard to remark that he wouldn't entertain riding it again unless he could take a thermos flask round with him.

And at this point, as you might well expect, Rosie took to her bed.

'It serves thee reight for listening to her,' Alf had chortled into Sam's glum features that night as they stood in the bar of the *Dog and Duck*.

'Can't understand it,' said Sam, slowly shaking

his cap covered head.

'I can,' said his grinning partner, 'Yer couldn't resist it, all of yer. Yer all knew what she is, but yer couldn't resist it, and does tha know why? Eh? It's cos yer wer all frightened to death in case she were right for once and yer missed out on it, that's why, yer set of chuffs. I wouldn't believe her if she told me me own name.'

'Ah, but look at the amount old Hudson put on it!' Sam protested. 'I mean, yer don't expect a clever bloke like him *not* to know what he's doing, do yer?'

'Hudson? He's spent t' last twenty-five bleeding year not knowing what he's doing! Christ, half of us daren't go to him. I wouldn't let him pick my nose, never mind a winner.

'I tell thee what, they should 'ave left that sodding horse back in t' stable and let Hudson ride Rosie round that course. Now *that* would 'ave been a safe bet!'

Curly Bradshaw didn't share Alf's mirth though. Ten quid of his carefully guarded profits had been invested into this abortive betting coup. Ten beautiful one pound notes which he had lovingly rolled up in a slip of paper with the word Parador and his each way forecast instructions carefully noted on it, surreptitiously slipped into Fats' hand with the excited expectation of seeing them return to him along with lots of their friends.

Only to experience the trauma, the sickening reality, that it was not to be. And that no matter how hard he may wish it they would never again gather dust in his secret place.

'Sick?' He'd bellowed over the counter at old Mrs Flynn when she had answered his furious enquiry about Rosie's whereabouts.

'She's not half as sick as me,' he'd yelled, violently wrapping up the quarter-pound of beef dripping she'd just asked for.

'That were money I'd put to one side towards one o' them freezer things, so I could 'ave started selling them ice lollies what all kids round here are going mad for.

And look what I do wi' it, I put it all on a chuffing useless lump o' dog meat what she tells us can't lose, and it does dun't it!

He'd had to pause for a minute then seeing as how he'd been squeezing the parcel so hard in his anger that all the dripping had slid out of one end and was now running down his trousers and onto his shoes. But it didn't deter him from what really hurt.

'I blame her!' He'd snarled, beginning to carve and weigh another lump on the scale. Then, glaring once again at the bemused old woman watching all of this, he changed his mind.

'No I don't,' he'd snapped aloud, 'I blame all of yer . . . I wouldn't have backed it if you lot hadn't'.

Then, thrusting the greasy parcel into her hands, he demanded: 'Ave yer any idea how long it takes me to make *that* kind of money round here?'

Well, Mrs Flynn who was no great lover of this notorious penny pincher, had withstood all of this tirade silently up to that point. But enough was enough. It wasn't her fault that he'd lost his money, all she had done was to answer his original query concerning the petrified Rosie's whereabouts.

So, pointing the greasy parcel at the three remaining hairs upon his otherwise naked head, she simply said into his screwed-up face, 'Tha'd 'ave been better off buying thissen a wig wi' it.' Then, pausing at the door before she left, she added into his stunned features, 'And if this dripping's as good as that horse what tha backed, it'll tek me a bleeding week to cook a pan of chips'.

The tinny bell above the door almost broke as she slammed it, completely drowning out Curly's desperate shouts that she hadn't paid for the dripping.

In the 1950s people used to come to Sheffield for a holiday, and just to prove it, Ann and Ernie sent a card to their Mum and Dad in Hove, saying that they were having a lovely time and that it was going too quickly! In those days all the cards were black and white and Wyming Brook Drive was much better looked after than it is today.

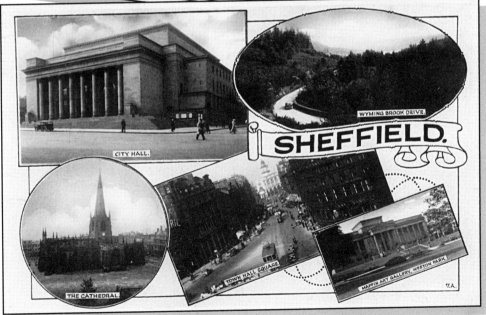

It was to be the best part of a week before Rosie dared to venture outside again, although it would have been sooner had it not been for the fact that she'd heard that Ria Thorpe of the deadly mouth was waiting for her. And I've no doubt that the prospect of getting a mouthful of that was enough to make her put her head back under the covers. You see, Ria's particular complaint over this whole disastrous episode was that she had done something which she had always held back from doing before when she'd been short of cash. She had pawned F... F... Freddie's beloved half-hunter pocket watch. The one which stretched back through Freddie's family to before the turn of the century. But she had been desperate for something which would have raised far more than the usual half-a-crown or more that came with the majority of pledges. So she had risked it. And having received the princely sum of two quid against its value she had followed the crowd, hadn't she? And lost the lot. Thanks, in her view anyway, to the beloved Rosie's red hot tip.

'It were his dad's tha knows,' she kept repeating to everyone that she met, as though their sympathy would make the betrayal seem less. Mind you, it might have done if she hadn't been soaking 'em at the same time with that jet of high powered spray which went everywhere with her. 'He dun't know that I've popped it yet,' she'd wailed at them. 'He'll go mad when he finds out, and all through her, that gobby chuff, wait till I see her, I'll shove this bleeding pawn ticket reight up her arse I will. What am I going to tell him if he looks for it, eh? He'll play hell he will, yer don't know him when he's roused.'

How the hell Freddie would manage to play hell with her or anybody else for that matter, baffled me. For one thing it would take him that long to get it out, he would ten to one forget what he was supposed to be upset about, and secondly, Freddie had long since learned that engaging Rosie in close combat argument got you just about as far as repeatedly ducking your head into the canal. But fair do's, he was upset and he did try.

Looking back on it all it truly was an abject lesson in the power which this particular sport wielded over our masses, and the gullibility of most of us when presented with the possibility of easy gain. Even when it is offered by a source previously considered to be unreliable.

I'm in no position to criticise those who fell for Rosie' misplaced forecast. It was in her nature to spread news, to be our Mercury, the messenger of the gods.

They chose to ignore her greatest failing of never getting her facts right on this occasion, and they paid for it, as all hasty people do. But then, neither can I blame them for abandoning their traditional mistrust of her when for once she brought tidings of great possible joy. They probably saw it as a double-edged opportunity of lining their pockets and having the pleasure of watching Fats Burns face as he grudgingly paid them out.

For without doubt, unlike the rich owner or breeder, the real pleasure lay just as much in beating the bookie as in the reward which went with it. And the fact that your occasional victory over him was scant recompense for the continual outlay made in achieving it didn't stop you from feeling the warm glow of success.

The likes of Gordon Richards, Harry Wragg, Charlie Smirke and the young Lester Piggot will always go down in racing annals as jockeys *par excellence*. Men with the consumate skill to extract the very best of qualities from these magnificent animals whose very existence is brought about by the wealthy.

But more than that. For such riders were idols to be exalted or cursed according to their performance. Makers or breakers of dreams to those whose lot in life fell far short in the way of being a winner. For a successful bet lifted the daily gloom of a boring routine and became a heavenly omen that despite whatever life may have denied you in many ways, Lady Luck had not deserted you altogether.

As Rosie Crapper would always begin, 'Yer'll not believe this'.

PROBABLY MY FIRST real awareness of female attraction occurred one Christmas when I would have been about six or seven. Quite young, I know, but I remember watching in astonishment as men suddenly displayed this apparently overwhelming urge to touch and kiss women.

Why this should be baffled me at the time, seeing as how they never showed the slightest inclination to repeat the contact at any other time of the year, well . . . not when there were others about to see it, anyway. In fact, I grew up believing it to be normal that a gap of at least a foot should always pertain between the two sexes, even when married, and especially when sat together in a pub.

So, as you will understand, kissing and hugging in front of others would seem to me at that time to be a complete breakdown in what I'd been led to believe was normal behaviour, even under the influence.

So why, I asked myself, did they do it? Why did a woman suddenly become desirable after closing-time on Christmas Eve when she had probably spent the last twelve months taking second place to her husband's other pursuits? I mean, let's face it, no fella could reasonably expect his missus to be content when she knew that there was many a time when he came home more excited about a good hand at crib than he was at seeing her.

So why didn't she object more, seeing as how she knew this? I mean she never missed a trick when it came to playing hell about his washing and queuing for his fags and getting the insurance man to 'leave it for another week'.

I don't know why I should have burdened myself with this conundrum when all the other kids I played with didn't give a monkey's what the men and women got up to so long as there was summat in their stocking on Christmas morning. But me, being what I am, couldn't be content with that.

Pictures of the Salvation Army in action are very hard to find. The best I could manage was this band going away from the camera in Woodhouse.

Which is a shame, because the Salvation Army was an important part of our lives, in the background perhaps, but one of those things like trams and gas lamps that you thought would always be there until you suddenly realise how long it is since you saw them in the pub on a Saturday night or playing on their way to the Citadel on Sunday morning.

What made them wrap their arms around each other and feel at bums at Christmas when they wouldn't dream of doing it at Easter or Whitsuntide? That's what I wanted to know, besides getting a little prezzy.

So, being a kid whose entire world at that time revolved around climbing drainpipes, collecting cigarette photo cards of all the football and boxing stars and whose only interest in girls was that they could always make their spice last longer, I came to the conclusion that there must be more to women than I knew of. They must, I reasoned, have some sort of special power, a kind of force field they could exert when it suited them, making men do things which normally they would reject out of hand as being sloppy or daft. And having reasoned all of that I decided to afford them far more credit than my elder contemporaries did. That way, I reckoned, I would be too smart for 'em should they ever try it out on me, or so I thought. Because it's one thing being a little clever clogs and thinking that you're wider than the rest, but the truth of all this was that all I had done in actual fact was to set myself apart from all of my growing-up mates who were quite content to wallow in their ignorance and enjoy all the titilating contact they were making with girls whilst Muggins here went without.

As far as they were concerned, if being lured into a back-entry by some nubile maiden with a gleam in her eye was being 'used', then *Hallelujah*, let it roll Maurice, and three cheers for being daft. No wonder they always had me acting as a lookout. If I'd have had more bloody sense I'd have been down the entry with 'em.

It was Harry Owen who cured me. Good old thick-as-pudding and 'I'll do owt' Harry Owen. And that in itself proves how big a mug I'd been in this matter right up to the age of fourteen, because I had spent years looking down on him for the way he had struggled at school trying to master the rudiments of reading and writing. Yet there he was, consistently leaving me feeling inferior to him due to his skill at pulling birds.

I just couldn't understand the sense of it. I mean, he wasn't smart to look at and he couldn't make 'em laugh, and he had been notorious in our class for the way the nurse would regularly find 'dicks' in his hair. And yet he could chat a lass up with a consumate ease which I found impossible to copy. In short, he dismantled completely all my theories about women's power over men, *and* my silly misconception that I was more clever than him. Consequently, I came to a revised decision. Harry wasn't as dumb as he seemed, and that I was the chuff for counting my fingers whilst he made more pleasurable use of his.

At that point I decided to grow up.

And I am grateful to him. But only for that, because without his example, I might still have been walking around Sheffield to this day shoving a miniature cross into any woman's face who dared to approach, and I would have missed out on the pleasure which a smashing family brings me now. I might have finished up as a premier expert on such barmy things as the Film Fun comic, or frog breeding from tadpoles, not to mention a diploma in the art of keeping watch for others. Harry saved me from that, and I owe him one.

So I changed, and being the sort who could usually make a joke out of most things, I was amazed how easily I could please most of them. My approach became one of subtlety and amateurish wit. Unlike Harry, he was openly brutal to the point where I saw him actually reduce them to tears, then walk away and think nowt of it.

Like Joan Wallis for instance. Now that poor lass had to grow up wearing white tape over one side of her glasses due to her other eye having this very bad squint in it. They did that then, the theory being that covering the good 'un would make the bad 'un work harder to right itself. Trouble was that it made her life a misery the way all the other kids made fun of her for the way her affected eye always seemed to be concentrated on her nose-end.

I could have wept for her at times, although I'll admit that it was off-putting talking to her, because no matter how hard you tried to avoid it you always finished up looking at her nose-end with her. All the same, she was a nice lass and Harry wanted shooting for the way that he treated her when she dared to suggest that he take her to the *Adelphi* cinema. She was desperate to see Errol Flynn in a film called *They Died With Their Boots On* at the time. But it didn't make any difference to him.

'Tha what?' he'd snorted contemptuously into her face. 'They'll have to show t' picture on t' floor for thee to watch it'. And then he walked away, oblivious to his own callousness and the tear running slowly down from her bad eye.

Even Errol didn't treat 'em that bad.

Mind you, Harry didn't always escape unscathed. Not everyone that he met was as meek as poor old Joanie, and there were times when he had to leg it.

Like when his mouth ran away with him that night when me and him and snotty Pete Fairfax were in the 'mugs' alley part of Attercliffe Skating Rink. It was there that he spotted this girl called Alice Cotton who was nervously making her way around this learner's area clutching tightly at the barrier which ran down the centre.

Now Alice had taken to visiting our end regularly over the previous couple of months with her mates in search of fresh lads, and had gained the dubious distinction of being popular amongst us for her 'generosity'. Anyway, Harry (paying scant attention to the two big lads fitting their skates on beside us), opens his big gob and calls out to her as she glided past us, causing one of these lads to give him a long hard look.

'Hey up,' he said coldly. 'Does tha know her?'

Now if he'd just said 'yes' and left it at that, there'd have been every chance that me and snotty Pete could have had our money's worth trying to skate like the rest, but he didn't did he. Harry just couldn't resist putting on the big 'I am' bit whenever anyone broached the subject of girls. So what does he do? He gloats and sneeringly replies that not only is he extremely familiar with this 'bint', but so were most of the rest of us as well.

By this point I had become uncomfortable, because the looks on both of their faces convinced me that they were far from impressed at what had just been imparted to them by this soft sod. So that when the next menacing probe of 'how's tha mean?' was put to Harry I decided forthwith that it might be prudent to remove the skates I'd just finished fitting to my shoes, mainly on the principle that I could run a hell of a lot faster without them.

'I mean she's easy,' the balm-pot had grinned at them, stupidly believing that he was still creating a big impression.

'Easy?' The taller of the two had growled as he rose to stand unsteadily on his skates. 'How easy?'

'Well . . .' says he of no brain, 'put it this way kid, her clouts 'ave been up and down more times than t' RAF.'

What happened then remains to this day as a mere blur to me. But I remember being laid on my side with this chair on top of me and feeling aggrieved that one of them should have banged me one on the

With hair by courtesy of Brylcreem these four teenagers are plainly from the mid-fifties era of cutaway collars, Windsor knots and hair-styles that came — along with kiss curls and Rock'n'Roll — from the other side of the Atlantic. For some reason they haven't grown long sideburns yet, but you can bet they have the beginnings of DAs on the backs of their heads. This is me and three mates around 1956, even though my children might not believe it!

A period cartoon from the *Morning Telegraph* of 1958.

"Well, there are **ONLY 7 days** in a week—how else can I fit you all in?"

ear when I hadn't so much as spoken a word to him.

And although I can remember scrambling across the floor like a crab in the fish market towards the door, I still took in the remarkable sight of Harry in full flight with the girl's brother hanging onto his coat with one hand whilst punching wildly at Harry's bobbing head with the other as he was towed at a furious rate around the rink.

It became chaos. There were bodies on their backs, doing the splits, hanging over the barrier and generally getting battered as these two barged around the rink in Harry's frantic attempt to escape. Girls were screaming, lads were cursing and the owner dashed from behind the skate counter to throw a sweeping brush at them. He missed and hit a kid of about six who'd been sat with his mother watching his elder sister skate, and the mother went berserk after the owner, and I thought 'sod this' and shot out of it.

I left Harry to it, and didn't stop running till I reached our front door.

The other one that I recall with relish about him was when he tried out his tactics on a Salvation Army girl he saw when we stood one day watching the citadel band marching down Staniforth Road

from Darnall. It had all the Sisters behind in their uniforms and bonnets, whirling those beribboned tambourines in intricate patterns before them as they lustily sang out:

'*Come and join us,*
Come and join us,
Come and join our happy band,
If you want to wear a bonnet
With the Sally Army on it,
Will you please put a penny on the drum,
Will you come?'

Well, Harry took one look at this particular young sister going past with them and he just flipped, and before we knew it we suddenly found ourselves, me and Sammy Gregory and snotty Pete, following on as he kept pace alongside of her, leering and winking into her embarrassed face as she did her best to sing with the others. The lust in his face that day was disgusting to watch as he openly made that helpless lass endure his unwanted attentions with snide comments of:

'What's thi name luv?'
'Wheer's tha live then?'
'Does tha allus wear them black stockings?'

All of this was shouted unashamedly above the music into her crimson face as she struggled to ignore his slobbering mouth no more than a foot from hers, and bravely soldier on with the rest. So that I almost cheered at the justice of it all when the gormy idiot walked with a bone-jarring thud straight into a gas lamp which was stood there quietly doing nowt.

I'll swear that it shook with the impact of him, that's how hard he hit it, so that by the time we reached him, he was sliding gently down it with this sort of bemused look about him. Without a doubt, God was looking after his own that day.

We sat Harry, near unconscious on the causey edge of the road and watched in delighted fascination as his right eyebrow slowly swelled into a magnificent lump that pulsed before our eyes as he sat there making these slow rolling movements of his head, not saying a word.

'Didn't tha see it?' I asked, laughing so much that it hurt as he gingerly touched this new dimension.

'No,' was all that he could manage, letting his injured head sink slowly down between his bent knees, 'Ah were too busy gawping at her legs.'

So we'd helped him up, the three of us, and walked him gently back to Salmon Pastures as the strains of the band faded into the distance, taking his dream with it.

But the best by far of all the disasters which punctuated his never ending search for more sexual experience has to be the graveyard episode.

Now that was when he'd coaxed little Madge Dunlop (of the enormous knockers) inside the gates of the Hilltop cemetery down in Carbrook one summer night whilst walking her back home to Whitworth Lane. Three hours he'd worked on her that night, walking her up and down the Common and making her giggle with his daft little jokes and his arm around her. His evil little mind racing through all of the likely and secluded places that he could steer her to.

And nowhere that he could think of was more secluded than the bone-yard after dusk. So, making up this cock and bull story about how his grandma's grave was just inside the gates, he'd dared her to follow him in and see the headstone. Surprisingly, she fell for it. God knows why, unless she saw it as some sort of challenge to overcome her natural fear. Either that or she was thick. Anyway, in she went, sticking to him tighter than Mae West's blouse and him trembling and sweating from a combination of fright and the prospect of showing Madge what 'raising the dead' really meant. So he picks out this headstone doesn't he, any one at random would do, and shoves a box of matches in her hand telling her to bend over and read the tribute, and as she did that he lost all control and grabbed at her with his hands flying up and down faster than Teddy Brown could play the xylophone.

Well she let out a yell and started squealing and struggling as she fell forward onto this stone doing her best not to finish up face down on the grave when up shoots this figure, no more than six foot away and just silently staring at them.

It paralysed 'em, with Madge forgetting where Harry had got his hand and him that mortified that he couldn't feel at what he'd got hold of anyway. Until the spell broke, and Harry went out of there like the road-runner, utterly abandoning the hapless Madge who by now was screaming her head off for him to wait as he left scorch marks going back up the Common. The 'ghost' was only two yards behind, breathing down his neck, no doubt just as anxious as Harry to gain the same amount of distance from the rooted Madge seeing as she was now making enough noise to make all those at rest complain.

He never again in his entire life ran as fast as he did that night. With his chest bursting and his eyes like chapel hat pegs, he almost cried in fear as those running feet kept up with him all the way back towards Newhall Road, only easing off when there was no more sound of them and he could stop to bend forward and grasp his shaking knees. Taking in great rasping breaths to ease his pounding heart and wishing like hell that he had achieved this condition from exertions with Madge rather then being chased by the 'ghost'. Whoever it was in there that night will always be a mystery to him and to us. Perhaps a heavy drinker who had stumbled in for a quiet snooze with it being a warm night. Or a Peeping Tom who'd seen them go in and had hoped to watch, or maybe just one of those eccentric balm- pots who get a kick from going into graveyards long after normal visiting hours, who knows?

Whoever he was he left an impression on poor old Harry which lasted a hell of a lot longer than anything that Madge could have done for him. I reckon that he should be eternally grateful that it happened when he was young and his heart could take it. 'Cos it would kill him now.

What followed can only be described as my growing up time as far as girls were concerned. A shared experience, a sort of inert desperation amongst us to obtain vital knowledge before the

army sent for us. As though going in as a virgin youth would somehow prevent you from being a proper soldier, making you an object of derision amongst those who had. So we chased it.

On street corners or secluded parts, then later in a score of Picture Houses and places like Fred Holmes on Infirmary Road or the *Roxy* at Page Hall. Just as lads do today, albeit in much more sophisticated places than we contended with. For I would imagine that today's night clubs are far better hunting grounds than the flea pits we sat in. Learning that frustrating lesson in this ancient ritual that girls can be the same as liquid mercury, almost impossible to grasp.

Still, it didn't blunt our awareness of their shape, or the hold which it can exert. Despite our lack of opportunity or the much stricter code of conduct demanded by fathers at that time.

I met many who, even at eighteen, still dare not apply make-up or lipstick before coming out if dad was there to see it. And I lost count of those who had to be home before the bewitching hour of ten, for it's no exaggeration when I say that the breaking of that curfew was often at the least a ban on any more nights out until they relented, or at its worst a damn good hiding. Hardly, you'll agree, ideal conditions for cultivating a fund of happy memories to take with us when the time came. In fact I felt tempted to write to the War Office asking them to hold on until I *had* made it.

Still, in truth, we did manage to find the odd moment of triumph, and I'm certain that the few lucky strikes which did come our way in those days were accepted with far more gratitude that they are now by youths who almost force-fed a diet of page three pin-ups, and parental apathy towards a daughter's best interests. We may not have had the plethora of today's liberated young ladies to make our dreams come true, but I don't see that now as a serious deprivation, or as a reason for stunted growth. Rather, I believe, is it a sign that human nature tends to elaborate upon the things which are out of reach. So that now I prefer to enjoy the down-to-earth logic in a tale once told to me by a fella that I worked with.

He told of two bulls in a field, one young and the other getting on a bit, with only a hedge separating them from a herd of attractive and willing young cows in the next. And the close proximity of such temptation and pleasure became too much for the young bull to endure any longer, so that unable to contain himself, he'd panted to the old 'un: 'I can't stand this any longer, look at 'em just stood there waiting for us, c'mon, let's run over there and get one apiece.'

But the old 'un held him back by saying:

'Tek thi time lad, tek thi time. If we *walk* over we can have the lot.'

Now that little piece of craftiness may not rank amongst the annals of great philosophy, but it certainly puts our youthful exertions into a proper perspective, because, like the young bull, I've no doubt that lads such as Harry would have gone over that hedge if it had have been Beecher's Brook, carrying the horse.

Such is illusion when it goes unchecked, and although it may have seemed different then, I can now see that our continual complaints of starvation in this matter were little more than childish pique. In fact, with hindsight, I feel a sense of relief, because unlike Harry, I never suffered the indignities of being chased on skates, or walking into gas lamps or being pursued by a 'ghost' up Attercliffe Common. And I seriously question whether what he went through in his quests was worth the pain of it all.

A fact brought home to me so vividly on the last occasion that I saw him when, to my delight, I realised that he looked very much older than I did. Proof indeed that whatever favours Lady Luck may have bestowed upon him then, she has saved for me later on.

Many thanks Harry for all the laughs, and may the roaring inferno of unbridled lust which consumed you then be no more than an ember now. 'Cos you're far too old to run now, old son.

Midland Station around 1958, with behind it one of the many stone terraces that still huddled on the Park hillside. Then a council that thought it knew better decided to replace them with Park Hill flats. The three trains are heading south to Derby and west to Manchester; the train to Catterick left from platform one.

W WITH ONE HAND gripping an old suitcase (in which I had meticulously arranged a clean vest and underpants, a shaving stick and razor, soap and towel, my ration book and a new toothbrush with a virgin block of Gibbs), I nervously made my way to the Midland Station.

It was absolutely pouring with rain, and I worried lest it should penetrate my raincoat and ruin the travel warrant and other papers that I was carrying pertinent to my long-awaited call-up. For I was finally on my way. Her Majesty had not forgotten me after all, and the excitement that I felt at it all blotted out the wet as I negotiated the first leg of a journey which was to take me to Catterick and the Royal Corps of Signals.

I remember that day so well, the thirteenth of October 1953, just as I remember the feelings which accompanied it. The sickly nervousness, panic almost, at the thought of leaving all the familiar things which previously I had been so desperately keen to say goodbye to. And yet elated and thrilled to be following all the mates who had gone in before me.

I recall telling myself that they too must have felt as I did. As, rain-soaked, I proferred the warrant at the window and received a single ticket in return. A licence to enter, for the very first time in my life, a daunting scenario of hissing steam engines which exuded an air of massive power even at a standstill. A gloomy and dismal picture of cold open platforms with linking bridges and equally cold-faced people who seemed determined not to speak to anyone else as they warily eyed the porters who pulled loaded trolleys behind them, shouting, 'mind yer backs' again and again.

Whilst from above, hidden I assumed amongst a

spider's web of steel framework in the roof, came the calm and posh-sounding voice of the announcer, looking down on all of this, I imagined, like it were some giant Hornby layout which he had the power to manipulate at his whim. And for a moment I'd wished that I was up there being him, and not me down here leaving home.

But I wasn't alone that day. Joyce, who I had met a few weeks earlier and been seeing often, had come, taking the morning off from her job at Woolworths, and my sister Betty with her husband Sam had come too, all of them there to 'see me off'. We stood in a small huddle waiting for the train to come, with the three of them trying hard to make me laugh and ease the tension. But it didn't.

And I remember anxiously scanning around me for signs of other young lads joining up like I was, someone to share the leaving with. But there were none, and I felt very much alone as the train came and someone said, 'this is yours', making me board it quickly, keen to move now, knowing that I couldn't stay or leave the station as they would once I had gone. Glad that the awful waiting bit was over.

I wanted to go, and yet I wanted to stay with them as I leaned out of that corridor window, doing my best to smile and make jokes as we all awaited the first jerk of the wheels, and I felt choked because it had never occurred to me as I'd counted off the days to going, that leaving people behind was also a part of the game, or that women let their eyes fill with tears as you left. Straining out to see them for as long as you could as they waved and called and Sam stuck a rigid thumb in the air, until the track curved and they were gone.

My journey was to be in two parts, first to Darlington, then on to Catterick, although I wasn't sure about the second part because no one had bothered to tell me. 'Go to Catterick,' was all it had said in the letter, and how I should get there from Darlington was to be *my* problem not theirs, and had I but known it I was being given my first lesson in army administration. Don't ask, just do it.

Anyway, I'd pushed it to the back of my mind and

settled down into the seat feeling glad to be out of the rain and on my way as the grey industrial carpet outside rolled by. And it gave me time to reflect as we steadily went through the old east end. Parts which I recognised from my growing-up time of short trousers with patches in them. And socks which had to be sewn up or darned.

Of going to school in a pair of clogs and 'slaring' for yards on the irons making the sparks fly. Of eating more than my share of bread and lard and of the thrill of being picked to play football for the school, despite having to wear boots two sizes too big which someone had given me. And *still* matching most of 'em at it.

The awful vulnerability we had felt when our father died before I had reached ten, envying those who still had that benefit and could enjoy the things which we couldn't, yet overcoming such things, such shortages in a patch and mend way, and laughing over it now.

We stopped at Doncaster, and a large heavy youth joined me in the carriage, and I remember feeling intimidated as, exuding an air of total confidence, he had thrown his case up into the mesh above me before bouncing down into the seat opposite. Bridging the gap between us by stretching his long legs to rest on the seat beside me.

I'd been careful not to notice, preferring instead to stare out the window as he lit a fag and blew the smoke noisily in my direction.

'Going in t' army kid?'

It was more of a demand than a question, daring me not to answer.

'Ah . . . I am,' I countered, making sure that my tone was less brutal than his and giving him only a cursory glance.

'Catterick?' He'd come back at me again.

'Ah . . . I am.' I repeated, hoping that it would all be as easy as this.

'What mob?'

'Sod off.' I thought, but didn't dare to say, so I complied:

'Royal Signals.'

It hadn't impressed him, I could tell, and suddenly I felt annoyed at myself for feeling so inferior, telling myself that my upbringing should have prepared me for this and that I was giving in too easily and that I wanted to hit back.

What abaht thee then?' I heard myself asserting, aggressively. He made me wait, shaping his mouth to blow perfect smoke rings before answering.

'Green Howards . . . hard cases . . . mind thee, it suits me, been down t' pit last three years tha knows . . . smartens thee up.'

Finishing off this piece of uncalled-for self idolatry into my sullen gaze with the contemptuous judgement that I would have been of little use down, there seeing as how I hadn't got 'enough meat on thee.'

Now that was too much. I mean, he was a lot bigger than me and obviously a lot stronger as well, but the rush of anger I had felt at this unnecessary insult demanded action. So I carefully weighed up the three options which seemed open to me.

One — thump him and take the consequences of it.

Two — kick his legs to one side and go outside in the corridor for a smoke to cool off.

Or three — pretend that he hadn't hurt me and eat the corned beef sandwich my mother had packed me for the journey.

After detailed thought into all of these I made my choice. As usual, she'd forgotten to put any piccallili on it.

The next one and a half hours in that lout's company convinced me that unless I quickly learned to stand my ground against his sort, my new life wasn't going to benefit me as much as I wanted it to. It was a clear warning to me that I would have to be incredibly naïve if I thought that he would be the only one of his kind that I would meet in the immediate future. But on this particular occasion, seeing as how I would probably never see him again, I'd decided to play safe and quietly suffer the barrage of bragging descriptions he was pumping out concerning the girls that he had 'seen to', and the

A rather worried looking squaddie in the 1950s. But my mum was proud of me!

fights he had won and the river of ale which he and his no doubt pig-ignorant gang of mates had supped. And I smiled to myself at it all, knowing that if I'd swallowed the whole of that then I would have been a bigger plonker than Big Ben. Because I knew different you see.

What he didn't know was that my old mate Herbert Lee's dad had been a collier down the Nunnery pit back home in Sheffield, and I was there that day with Herbert and Sammy Gregory when Mr Lee shot down their cellar steps and wedged the door behind him to keep old Dr. Hudson at bay when he turned up to lance this king-size boil on his bum.

49

there for nearly four hours, long after old Hudson had packed his cutter away and gone home, making it patently obvious to all of us kids that even big tough guys like him could be scared. So this clown opposite me that day had no chance with his superhuman bit that he was putting across about miners, not after what I'd seen that day.

And remembering that cheered me up no end, so that by the time we finally reached Darlington the stupidity of this cretin was something that I was inwardly laughing at rather than feeling hopelessly inadequate to. I felt dead chuffed at the way in which I had used logic to mentally whittle him down to size, vowing to myself that in future no matter what the degree of intimidation I would deal with it likewise. Whatever I lacked in size or strength I would compensate for by my ability to disect their exaggerated image or threat. *That* would stop any of them from getting the better of me, or so I thought.

Then I met my first NCO.

Now, there are certain things in this wide world which make the rest of us poor mortals stand back in awe from. The natural and unlimited power of Niagra Falls for instance or the excitement and danger of the Grand National, perhaps the technology of recent space travel or the unrivalled elegance and class of a Rolls Royce. Each and every one of them overwhelming us by their existence, so that we feel puny by comparison.

Well, for me, you can add to that impressive list another one, and that is a raw recruit's initiation to his first NCO. Because not to put too fine a point on it, he frightened seven different kinds of shit out of me that day.

We were on the station platform, about twenty of us, feeling totally at a loss as to what we should do next. Some had gathered in small groups to smoke and make idle chat, whilst others, like me, held back, warily watching for someone to act positively so that we could follow, when suddenly he was there, or rather the four of them were, with their battle dress tunics and trousers sporting razor-sharp creases, their belts and gaiters immaculately

I can only describe it as being hilarious watching Herbert's mother on her hands and knees in the street shouting down their cellar grate pleading with her terrified husband to 'come up and have it done, luv.'

It didn't seem to bother him that others in the street were witnessing his cowardice to drop his kecks for the aforesaid doctor to do his business. He just kept shouting back up for her to, 'sod off, he's not coming anywhere near me wi' that bleeding knife, I'll stick to bread poultices first.'

And he meant it, because he stuck it out down

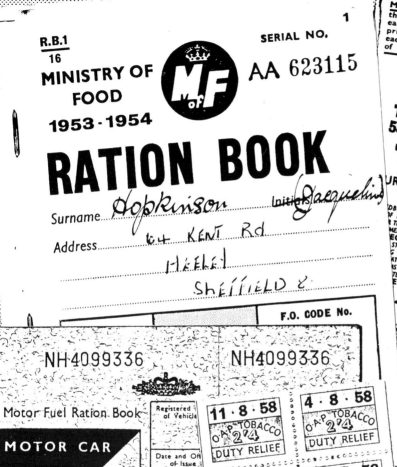

R.B.1
16

SERIAL NO.

1

MINISTRY OF FOOD

1953·1954

AA 623115

RATION BOOK

Surname... *Hopkinson*   Initials *Jacqueline*

Address... 64 KENT Rd

HEELEY

SHEFFIELD 2

F.O. CODE No.

NH4099336   NH4099336

Motor Fuel Ration Book

MOTOR CAR

1501 – 2200 C.C.

14 – 19 H.P.

Registered of Vehicle

Date and Off of Issue

This book is the property of Her Majesty's Government

The coupons in this book authorise the furnishing and acquisition of the number of units of motor fuel specified on the coupons.

11·8·58 O.A.P. TOBACCO 2/4 DUTY RELIEF	4·8·58 O.A.P. TOBACCO 2/4 DUTY RELIEF
28·7·58 O.A.P. TOBACCO 2/4 DUTY RELIEF	21·7·58 O.A.P. TOBACCO 2/4 DUTY RELIEF
14·7·58 O.A.P. TOBACCO 2/4 DUTY RELIEF	7·7·58 O.A.P. TOBACCO 2/4 DUTY RELIEF
30·6·58 O.A.P. TOBACCO 2/4 DUTY RELIEF	23·6·58 O.A.P. TOBACCO 2/4 DUTY RELIEF

MAXIMUM. No person may hold or have an interest in more than (A) 500 unit Certificates (purchase price 15/-, 15/6 or 16/- each) whether of one Issue or a combination of Issues at these prices, (B) 250 unit Certificates of the £1 Issue (purchase price 20/- each). These latter Certificates may be held even if the maximum of 500 units in the other Issues has or has not been reached.

T 58

479 403

NOT NEGOTIABLE

SEVENTH ISSUE

DAZ 00364

HOLDER'S REGD. No.

1 UNIT

PURCHASE PRICE 15/-

...D BY THE LORDS COMMISSION-... OF HIS MAJESTY'S TREASURY ...R THE AUTHORITY OF ACT OF ...MENT 10 & 11 GEO.V.c.18s 59 ...ECT TO THE PROVISIONS ...STATUTORY REGULATIONS ...G TO NATIONAL SAVINGS ...ATES THE PERSON REG-... THE HOLDER OF THIS ...TE IS ENTITLED TO ...EN YEARS AFTER ...HEREOF THE SUM

·0·6

NATIONAL SAVINGS CERTIFICATE

£1·0·6 AFTER TEN YEARS

20 MR 46

SHILLINGS 10

C23 164972

coated in green blanco and the toe caps of their boots dazzlingly reflective, even on a grey day like that. And I clearly remember how the crunch of their studs upon that platform as they reached us killed stone dead the chatter. We all stood there gob struck, even the lout that I had ridden with, all putty in their hands, without them having to speak a single word to achieve it.

Now, that is what I term as 'having effect'.

Well, they herded us together clutching our cases and things, with each and every one of us trying desperately hard to do everything exactly as they ordered it lest we be the one to get it wrong, or do it too slow, and incur whatever terrible punishment your fertile imagination had already convinced you they were capable of, so that it was a relief when they marched us out.

Well . . . I say marched, it was more of a governed walk, with this sergeant at the front and the other three acting like sheepdogs side and rear, until we were standing on the station front with this sergeant shouting out names from a clipboard and making jerking movements with his pen towards two waiting three-ton army lorries as each lad identified himself.

Eventually I found myself standing alone, baffled and worried as to why he hadn't named me, and acutely aware that the four of them were now eyeing me up and down like I was a tramp's vest.

'Who the frigging hell are you?' said the sergeant.

'Hartley,' I mumbled, saying the name almost apologetically, sick at being the one to spoil everything for them.

He just glared at me as though I had done it on purpose before remarking to the others that he'd once 'had a dog called that' before once again perusing the list.

'You,' he said to me finally, 'are not here, not on my list to be here, which means that I don't frigging know you, and what's more I don't *want* to frigging know you! Understand?'

And with that they all went to get on the trucks now filled with all those others which I'd assumed in all my unknowing innocence that I would be part of. But I wasn't, was I? I was just stood there on my own, feeling clueless, useless and shatteringly lost with two lorry-loads of so-called fellow recruits revelling in my lonely predicament.

'What am I supposed to do then?' I shouted out in desperation as the engines burst into life, not believing that they would just go and leave me without a single thread of advice to help me out.

He just wound down the cab window and looked at me for a few seconds before answering:

'Find yourself a skirt and crack on that you're in the WRACs son,' was all that he said. Then, seeing my puzzled look, he added, 'they're picking a load of 'em up here later on.'

And that was it, just that final sarcastic insult to my plea for help and they were gone.

Now no-one had told me that it was going to be like that. I mean, I had laboured under the naïve impression that soldiers stuck together. They did in all those films we'd watched, but this sodding lot weren't. Well, actually *they* were sticking together, it was just the fact that they weren't letting me stick together with 'em, that hurt. They didn't give a toss for me that day, and I felt disgusted with them for it seeing as how I'd left home to be with them.

Anyway, pulling up the wet collar of my mac for the umpteenth time that day I started to walk away from the station telling myself that it was just an initial test upon my capabilities to stand on my own two feet and that they could shove their stinking lorries up their arses, preferably with that clever-mouthed sergeant's head sticking out. I determined to myself that I would reach Catterick with or without them and that while-ever I had a tongue and two feet to carry me, I wouldn't be licked, adding to the satisfaction which I would feel at sticking two fingers up behind that clever sod's back when I got there.

And with those furious thoughts driving me on I strode purposefully out into the incessant rain, heading for the bus station, only to stop once more in complete dismay as my battered old case burst open spilling its contents around me in the wet, and the brand new block of Gibbs slowly, tantalisingly, rolled down a grate. I knew then that fate had decreed that my day should be a trying one.

Climbing aboard that bus is as fresh in my mind now, despite it being almost forty years ago, as though it were yesterday. My hair was plastered to my head, one shoe was leaking like a sieve at the welt, I was having to carry the old case under my arm to keep it together, and thinking that considering it was supposed to be a milestone in my life I'd have been better off overlaying that morning. I mean, I'd never gone so long before without seeing somebody that I knew, and I didn't like Darlington either, it wasn't as busy as Sheffield.

'Where to?' came the voice, breaking the grip which self-pity had swamped me with. It was the conductor, balancing in the aisle alongside me as the bus moved off.

'Catterick.' I shot back at him, trying hard to sound composed and in charge of the situation, finishing with a defiant 'Ah'm joining up.'

'Thank Christ for that,' was all he said with what seemed to be a combination of disinterest and sarcasm, 'I've been worried for ages.'

I just stared at him blankly, trying to look unhurt by his wit. Anyway, I couldn't see any reason to explain any further where I was going beyond what I had already told him. But he did.

'What part?' was his next one.

Somehow I resisted the urge to return his sarcasm by saying 'all of me,' and countered instead by telling him I didn't know.

'They just said come to Catterick.' I shrugged.

I remember him having this 'seen it all before' look on his face as, shaking his head, he'd asked if I had any idea how big Catterick was.

I answered that with a shake of mine. I didn't even know where the bloody thing was, never mind its size. Why couldn't things be simple? Why couldn't I have been taken there along with the others? Why did it have to be *me* stuck on a foreign bus in a place I'd never heard of before trying to tell him where I

was supposed to be without actually knowing where it was?

He must have realised that I was struggling because at that point he made an effort to help by asking what unit I was joining.

'Royal Signals.' I said.

'And didn't anyone meet you?'

I blurted out to him then what had happened and how I had been contemptuously abandoned at the station and how I was now doing my best to get there under my own steam.

'Oh!' he said, 'they went without you then?'

And then his face slowly broke into a mischievous grin which had gradually spread to lighten up the whole of his face.

'I've got some bad news for you lad,' he'd almost chortled with vicious glee. 'We're not taking yer either, yer on the wrong bus, you want the one going to Richmond.'

And once again I found myself back in the rain, with a good half-a-mile walk to squelch back to the bus station to the obvious amusement of he who had just given me the good news, grinning at me through the window as it pulled away.

It was by now almost three o'clock in the afternoon and seeing as I had left Sheffield nearly six hours previously and that the total journey time (with help) shouldn't have been more than three-and-a-half hours, you can understand my feelings being somewhat disturbed. *Nothing* had gone right for me so far. The weather, the company on the train, the abortive reception at the station and now the ignominy of being laughed at. Obviously there were going to be many things in my new life for which I was unprepared, and the thought that there was to be no more going back home at night to escape the problems that were being heaped upon me that day I must admit did tend to influence my mood.

I had a lot to learn, this wasn't mucky old Sheffield where everyone talked like I did and I could feel confident in being a part of it. This was a strange place full of people who wouldn't help you and, real or imaginary, the sense of rejection which I'd felt rekindled the determination that had surfaced when the trucks went without me. I *would* get to Catterick, with or without them. And throwing defiance to all including the weather I'd said out aloud:

'Yer can all bollocks!!!' before treading into another deep puddle.

It was to be an obscenity that I would use many times in those first few weeks of army life, and should the reader find its use offensive, I can only plead that when you are thrust into a world where even a lowly lance-corporal assumes the greatness of one of God's apostles, where those who are sent to teach you assault your disbelieving eardrums with an endless repertoire of magnificent insults, the like of which defy being repeated, then I give you my word that even *you* would have joined me in its heartfelt pronunciation.

But not within their hearing, lest you should find yourself paying the price of such rebellion by doing 'jankers'. Confined to barracks to perform the most dirty and menial of tasks so as to satisfy their impregnable ego. And their obvious pleasure at the power they wielded, expurgating the very last strands of defiance which might still fleetingly linger within you.

'Welcome to the British Army,' they barked.

'Now, on the command, you will all bend forward and place your heads between your knees . . . and on the second command of whistle, you will all render that much loved signature tune to the Archers up your waiting jacksies . . . now . . . *squaaad* . . . *BEND!!! squaaad . . . WHISTLE!!!*

And you did.

With that, and more similar indignities, they first reduced and then remoulded young lads like me into trained units, bringing to us the previously unknown satisfaction which comes from knowing that you are a part of something far bigger than anything else that you have ever known before, a pride in proving yourself capable of matching all of the others sharing with you in the guard duties and the route marches. The injections, the drill and weapon training and the spit and polish and bullshit which is heaped upon you in deliberation to see if you will crack and defy them.

But you don't, you take it all rather than be the one to let the squad down, it's called self-discipline, it is the backbone of the army and the architect of order.

All that I have left from those marvellous three and a half years now are photographs and memories, images to recall with relish in the protection of middle age, knowing that they can't get at me now. Yet, in truth, I wouldn't have missed them for anything. I *wanted* to go, *needed* to, and I welcomed it. For they were a forming and learning part of my life which I shared with so many of my generation. A lesson which even now I still benefit from when I look around in this later society which tolerates the vicious thug, the lack of example to children or the disregard which Thatcherism displays towards those unable to compete. None of it can remotely compare to the qualities of self-discipline and helping your mates.

And should you brand that as no more than sentimentality for a bygone time, let me add that the end product of that long gone experience is today reflected in the law abiding and thoughtful family that I am the head of. A sentiment I know which can be echoed by so many more who yearn for today's youth to be given the same start in life.

It was my time, one of the treats which life has bestowed upon me, and it will stay with me forever. For they took me from the streets and mucky workshops and the limited local contact that I had only known and introduced me to others from all four corners of this land. English and Scots and Irish and Welsh, with accents and customs I could never have imagined, broadening my mind far beyond the restricted confines shackling it in my early years.

As that sergeant would have put it, I 'got fell in'.

Thank you for your time, gentlemen. It was my pleasure to be insulted by you.

10
Dancing on the cobbles

Hoyland Street, Brightside, celebrates the end of the War in May 1945, with a tea-party beneath home-made bunting in a yard. So many happy faces, and the children in this glimpse of a day that needed solemn recording will still only be in their fifties. Where are they now?

T HE GRIMY LITTLE house that I was born into is long gone now, along with all of the others amongst which it huddled, giving so many of us our entry into this world. Our starter for ten, without the bonus. Soot-laden and basic in its construction, with an attic, then a single first-floor bedroom sitting atop the one lower room which served to provide us with the means for living together. As well as the cooking and washing and eating.

A place full of wet washing on a line in winter, where a bare wooden table took up too much room and too many bodies shared too little space. A miniscule patch which somehow whole families shared despite it being even further reduced by the necessary obstacles of a boiler and a cold water sink. So that when you take in the then common practice of having large broods, (often reaching double figures), you perhaps perceive a glimmer of what living down there in the 'thirties must have been like for families born to it.

There were nine in ours, although two never made it past their infancy. But then, that too was common.

My sister Violet had a girl friend whose mother bore twenty- two, and lost most of them. Victims, like so many more to poor health, inadequate diet and the ravages of consumption and pneumonia from the cold and the damp. Killers topped up with the added perils of scarlet fever, ricketts and rheumatic fever. For death was a frequent visitor to those not yet old, and illness was the price to pay for having less medical knowledge. It was a time when long-term unemployed fathers like ours stood in idle groups on street corners praying for the jobs to come back, and grey-faced wives dreaded breaking the news of yet another pregnancy. Knowing that it would start its life sharing a bed and living on milk pobs.

A time when a weekly 'relief' of one pound sufficed to pay the rent, and what was left had to be supplemented with ten bob's worth of food vouchers to spend at Gallons grocery shop in the everlasting battle to feed everyone. A pittance which always expired long before the next bit of relief was due.

Financial hardship which made musty-smelling pawnshops our saviour. So often the difference between having food on a newspaper-lined table and going without. Borrowed aid for which kids like me stood in long queues, with your mother, or elder sister and brother. Waiting and waiting to enter this place filled with long shelves, each one packed with layers of paper-wrapped parcels with tickets attached to denote where they really belonged, when the owner could afford it. A vast array of clothes and ornaments, of tools and bedding, along with books, shoes, medals and pocket watches and almost anything that you could imagine. All from men and women who gave up the only coat they had in winter and even their wedding rings until some money came once more, making it possible to renew their ownership.

Yes, pawn tickets were a part of our education, our 'O' levels. Our learning of how to make do long before Bevan's vision of the Welfare State came into reality. So that, having no wish to make light of the worry and fear which came in the 'eighties, when our industrial world collapsed, you will excuse me if I seem less impressed than some when we talk about the hardship of now.

I take a view which tells me that today's conception of being deprived is far removed from such things suffered during that depression. In those times, four or five or even more would share a flock-mattressed bed, equally divided top and bottom with coats making up for the lack of proper bedding. And feet became a part of your pillow.

Where bugs and blacklocks and rats and mice were infestations which even the most fastidious of cleaning failed to eradicate completely. Where cellars flooded deep enough to sail tin baths in and kids were scrubbed in boilers and grown-ups made do with a wash, or hung on for a weekly sojourn at Attercliffe slipper baths to luxuriate for a wee while in the deep hot water, cleansing away the feel of dirt with carbolic, renewing the feel of smooth skin.

A time when electricity didn't reach us until after my birth, making light a blessing after so many years of squinting by the glow of candles or gas mantles or paraffin lamps. A time where the relieving of nature was accomplished in a freezing outside latrine, or in a stinking bucket at the top of the stairs. Hygiene, privacy and decorum were strangers in a house which had no hot water on tap, had too many bodies in it and where the ordeal of being faced with a cold midnight walk discouraged even the most discerning.

It was a time when children of the poor were taken to a Christmas feast at the Cutlers' Hall, to be fed and given a simple gift by those better off who felt moved to be charitable at that festive time. And it was good of them, for I know that my elder brothers and sisters were grateful, but a rag doll or a wooden sword didn't lengthen a coat that was well past its sell-by date and had already been handed down twice.

It was a time when heat only came after standing for hours in bitter cold and wet weather to buy two bags of coke which were then pushed all the way back in a battered pram. When good neighbours and a midwife riding a bike made up the complete delivery service for new-borns, and the most degrading of all, a time when you accepted the humiliation of having your belongings compulsorily 'stoved' in a fumigation van before the council granted you the blessing of a new estate house, making sure that we didn't take our little friends with us.

That was an obnoxious, though often necessary, regulation which made women weep in shame and men turn away in anger, knowing that to refuse was to lose the chance long waited for, unable to object as their bits and pieces were unceremoniously cleansed. And this within my lifetime, in a city which proudly displayed the finest silverware money could buy in polished oak-lined showrooms to those whose social position protected them from the dirt of the East End and Neepsend and Heeley and all the other parts of Sheffield which shared such housing and dreamed of sleeping bite-free.

Were such a measure employed today, I have little doubt that public and Social Service reaction to it would be far more pronounced now than the meek acceptance of then. For we are different now, we have tasted the sweet wine of comfort. And they can shove their flat beer.

Now, thankfully, such things are gone, and rightly so. We have moved on through an era of work and wages and improvements which made us falsely believe that the good life would last forever. Believing that the solid forty-year-old foundation of constant employment would never give way . . . until it did. Making us hate those who proved us to be wrong as we signed on the dole for the first time, disdainful of the questions being asked by girl clerks young enough to be our daughters.

Many of us were able to conjure up a mental flashback of what it must have been like in the 1930s. So that I dimly understood those nine long years my own father had spent like that. Years in which his brood grew larger as the house got smaller. Waiting for things to change.

Now it's our turn to accept the new, to throw our past into the fumigation van so that we can enter the squeaky clean Sheffield they are building for us. It has no place in it for all the old landmarks we grew up with and which we used as pointers in the stories we have told, making the stories harder to tell. But it won't stop us wanting to tell them. Like the way when we huddled as kids in those terrible nights spent in air raid shelters as searchlights probed inky black skies seeking out the unseen drone of German bombers.

Nights of noise and the smell of damp clothes and crying and urine. Of the earthen floor trembling and the muffled crunching of distant ack-ack guns doing their best to help us. Fully conscious, even as a five-year-old, of the oppressive silent fear all around me. Broken only by the whispered 'that weren't far off,' as yet another bang shook us.

Then later, of going to school with a gas mask in a box threaded with string slung over my shoulders, searching the gutters for lumps of shrapnel grotesquely shaped by the heat of their impact upon us. Of seeing the letters 'SP' painted on house walls to denote that a styrup pump was available to fight the dreaded incendiaries, alongside the cold haunting wails of the sirens rising and falling, telling us that the bombs were coming again.

So that we hit back in our childish way by making fun of Adolph. Sticking a lateral finger under our noses to represent his daft moustache as we goose-stepped around the school yard giving the Nazi salute and singing to the tune of *Colonel Bogey* of how Hitler had 'only got one ball'. Ridiculing him in comparison to the heros we made of the Spitfire and the Lancaster bomber and General Montgomery's Eighth Army as the wireless told us of their stirring deeds. Spurred on by the emotive rhetoric of Winston Churchill and *Workers' Playtime*.

Such are my early memories. A childhood spent, like so many more, dominated by shortages and permeated by uncertainty in dark streets made blacker by the rule of having to prevent the smallest glimmer of light escaping and giving the enemy any clue as they searched for us. Whilst above us rode the huge silvery-bodied barrage balloons, bobbing on their wires in silent sentry watching over us.

Until the day when we all rejoiced with huge bonfires when the last 'All Clear' sounded and we threw the black-out blinds in the bin. Filling whole streets with streamers and Union Jacks, with the women somehow laying on piles of sandwiches and jelly with weak custard and home-made tarts for everyone to join in. Washing it all down with endless tea served from those large stainless urns which always came out for a funeral. Surrounded by 'Victory' signs daubed on wall after wall, and even on the roofs.

And there were the white-washed messages of 'Welcome Home Joe' or whatever the lucky one's name might be, teaching us at an early age that patriotism is a powerful thing.

I'm glad that I knew it. Glad to have shared such times before the electronic wonderland arrived, Taking away the pleasure of simple things like our annual treat of having something new to wear for Whitsuntide. Parading along your street on the Sunday morning and knocking on doors to stand like a Burton's dummy showing them off. To have a penny and even the odd threepenny bit stuffed into your brand new top pocket, doubling the treat.

'Is dem thi new clooers?' They'd say in exaggerated admiration, making you swell with delicious pride and pose even more stiffly than ever.

'Well, look after 'em waint tha,' they'd say, 'tha'll not get any more till next year'.

And you knew they were right.

Then we'd spend their donations on treats like sticky 'Marry-me-quick,' with the little 'uns getting it all over their faces and sticking their eyes up solid, causing mothers to play hell as they'd grasp the offending face in a headlock whilst vigorously pummelling away at the sightless sockets with a flannel. Swearing away at the squawking kid saying 'How many times 'ave I teld thee to keep it in thi gob!'

And I remember taking a hot oven plate wrapped in a cloth to bed with us on freezing nights to warm our feet on. Until, usually in the middle of the night, it would work its way out to fall with an almight crash which shook the entire house and brought forth startled complaints of 'Christ . . . what was that?'

And women pickling onions months before Christmas, standing the tall jars on high shelves until the time came to bite them and all your features screwed up and even your teeth hurt at the sheer power of their sourness.

Then reaching fifteen and finally joining the grown-up world of work which gave us meagre financial treats like buying sheet music song books from Woolworths. Having singalongs to the latest songs long before Max Bygraves made his fortune at it.

Or we stood in those little booths in Cann's down Dixon Lane, listening for nowt to the records of Frankie Lane or the Platters on the pretext that we'd be buying it although we hadn't got a tanner between us, till they'd twig on and take the record off. Still, there was always Jack Jackson on a Saturday dinner-time.

Sometimes we would push our way into the headscarved and flat-capped tide of humanity which ebbed and flowed along the aisles of the old Rag and Tag market, between Dixon Lane and the bottom of Commercial Street. And there'd be rain running down your neck from the canvas tops of the stalls which you couldn't do anything about because your arms would be pinned down by the sheer crush. Defenceless against the jabs of flying elbows or the tread of big feet as shopping baskets gave you vicious digs where it always hurts the most.

God knows how many women's bums got felt at in there, but there was always one yelling out and taking a swipe at some poor sod who was, in her opinion anyway, the guilty party. And that could turn nasty if he'd got his missus with him and she didn't believe him either.

Ask anyone about the old Rag and Tag and watch their eyes light up as they recall the pottery stall where complete dinner services were assembled, locked together then thrown eight feet across the stall to be caught by his assistant, never dropping one. Or the pups and pigeons and rabbits and bright yellow day old chicks we bought, smuggling them home under our coats on the tram or bus, hoping they wouldn't yelp or coo or wriggle or cheep and get us chucked off. Yes . . . the good old Rag and Tag, where you were lucky to emerge wearing the same coat.

Or we'd stand watching bobbies doing point duty

in their long white macs in the rush hour, directing traffic with their decisive hand and arm movements. Defying any argument from those who sought to do it differently. Not like now, when foul language and intimidation appear to be an integral part of the Highway Code. Put your indicator on today and you can go where the hell you like.

And do you remember the way each murky November we would pay our silent respects for two minutes to those who gave their lives for us? When shops and factories and traffic and ordinary people stood without a sound, no matter where they were, to say that they hadn't forgotten. If only they did it now, just to show our kids that there have been far greater events in our history than buying *Neighbours* from Australia. And on a lighter note, what about those *Health and Beauty* magazines we all pored over as youths. Full of nude women throwing beach balls or playing tennis. Wearing nowt but a big smile, despite standing on sharp pebbles or bashing some tender bit with the racquet as a bitter cold wind turned all their lips blue. And

Another children's party, this time in Little London Road in 1953 for the Queen's coronation. Although it's only eight years since the austerity of 1945, there are now paper serviettes on the tables and party hats on many heads. And sweets, sugar and eggs are off ration.

At the back stand the organisers, who have taken a day away from Rinso and Oxydol and lighting the fire with the *Sunday Empire News* to toast a new queen and take the first faltering steps into what we believed would be a bright new era.

no matter how hard you tried you could never see the bit that mattered, 'cos it was always painted out. I know . . . we spent hours under gas lamps trying to make it fade. But it never did.

And it was just as frustrating in all those Mickey Spillane or Hank Janson books we avidly read. Because without fail the red hot chapters always ended just as this feller was about to join the gorgeous girl in bed. They did it on purpose, knowing that you'd be reading at ten times the normal speed and then, there'd be this line of dots. Nowt else — just dots . . . And you'd be up half the sodding night trying to use your imagination filling 'em in.

And talking of being kept awake, what about the *Man in Black* on the wireless? Him with the horrible laugh telling murder stories which frightened the life out of me. He had this deep and menacing voice which really put the wind up you. It did me anyway. In fact, I daren't go up our stairs after he'd done in case he was under the bed. So I used to push my little sister up first . . . just in case.

Sorry Pat, blame him for being too good!

Believe it or not, but I must have been about eleven or twelve before I ever saw a real live black man. And that came about when my grandma took in two newly arrived West Indian lodgers.

I recall sitting in her house gaping at them as they chatted away to her in their funny sounding accent, marvelling at their shiny white teeth and their ill-fitting suits and gaudy ties. Obviously, I wasn't to know that I was witnessing the advance guard for the thousands who would follow them to bring a new dimension to our way of life. All that I knew was that here was something in real life which previously I had only seen on the pictures. Usually playing the part of butlers to rich white families in America's deep south, saying things like 'yessum' all the time.

Or they were Paul Robeson paddling a canoe in *Saunders of the River*, singing (what sounded like anyway) 'Ai-ee-oko' as they took the white commissioner to see some great chief. Either that,

or they all got dolled up in warpaint and waved their spears about like tic-tac men as they dragged this screaming white bird off into the jungle. With Johnnie Weismuller as Tarzan, swinging twenty seven miles through the trees before dropping down to give 'em all a good pasting and taking her back.

Or he might dive eighty-odd foot down into this lake to have a scrap with the biggest crocodile you've ever seen. It had a mouth wider than the Wicker Arches and a set of teeth that Carmen Miranda would have killed for. But it didn't frighten him. Twenty minutes he'd be under water tussling with this bugger, in fact you could go out for a pee and a smoke and still get back before he came up for a breath. And all the time Cheetah, his monkey, would be doing back flips and covering its eyes to make you think he wouldn't make it. We must have been dafter than the monkey for watching it.

Anyway, you can now understand my perplexity at that time (after watching such garbage) as to why these two black feller's could sit there like that without Johnnie coming flying in through my grandma's window to get at 'em. So I decided that it must be because we'd got no trees.

Then there was Wilson in the *Wizard* comic. Now *he* was over a hundred years old yet could still beat all of the world's best athletes. He lived in this cave on the moors and ran twenty miles every morning before swimming in an icy river, even in winter. The soft sod, at his age and all. And Alf Tupper, the 'Tough of the Track' in the *Victor*. Now he was the one who'd work a twelve hour shift, thumb a lift to a meeting two hundred miles away, have a bag of chips, then knock six seconds off the mile record, and still be back in time to clock on next morning. Can you get your breath? Thatcher would have made him a knight.

As well as Dan Dare in the *Eagle* as he piloted into the future with his mate Digby to fight the Mekon. Mind you, it was a good comic was that, very informative and futuristic. It made Flash Gordon's rocket look like an Austin Seven, with PC 49 driving it.

Whitsuntide was always a good time for us. Thousands of Sunday-school kids filled the parks to sing, many in new once-a-year' clothes. Streets rang with early morning bugles and drums as columns of scouts, guides and the Boy's Brigade proudly marched behind their banners.

On Staniforth Road, on the opposite page, on Whit Monday in 1950 huge crowds turned out to watch the floats and tableaux which made up the annual Darnall Medical Parade. Nowadays we stay at home and watch a video instead.